Teaching *comprehension* strategies

Developing reading comprehension skills

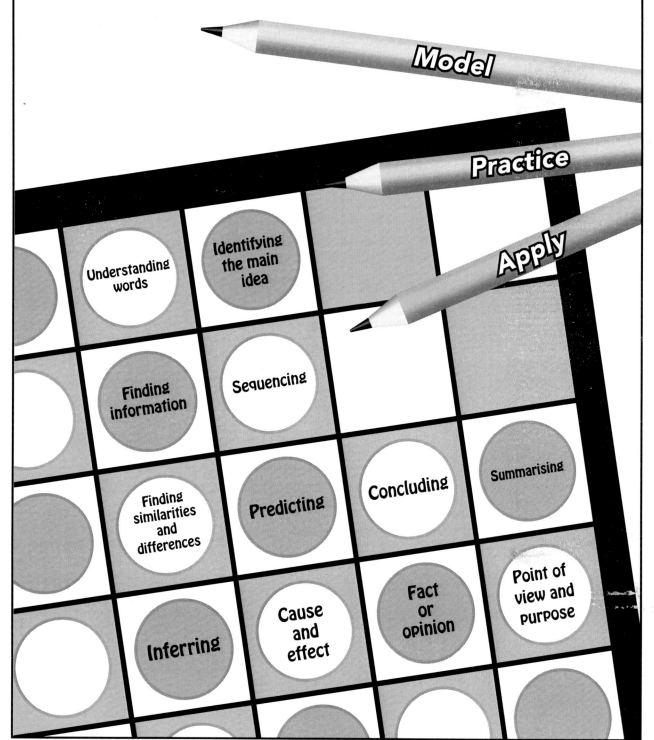

Model

Practice

Apply

Understanding words

Identifying the main idea

Finding information

Sequencing

Finding similarities and differences

Predicting

Concluding

Summarising

Inferring

Cause and effect

Fact or opinion

Point of view and purpose

Prim-Ed Publishing

TEACHING COMPREHENSION STRATEGIES *(Book D)*

Published by Prim-Ed Publishing 2007
Reprinted Prim-Ed Publishing 2014, 2016
Copyright© R.I.C. Publications® 2006
ISBN 978-1-84654-120-9

PR–6299

Additional titles available in this series:
TEACHING COMPREHENSION STRATEGIES *(Book A)*
TEACHING COMPREHENSION STRATEGIES *(Book B)*
TEACHING COMPREHENSION STRATEGIES *(Book C)*
TEACHING COMPREHENSION STRATEGIES *(Book E)*
TEACHING COMPREHENSION STRATEGIES *(Book F)*
TEACHING COMPREHENSION STRATEGIES *(Book G)*

Internet websites
In some cases, websites or specific URLs may be recommended. While these are checked and rechecked at the time of publication, the publisher has no control over any subsequent changes which may be made to webpages. It is *strongly* recommended that the class teacher checks *all* URLs before allowing pupils to access them.

View all pages online   **Website:** www.prim-ed.com

Foreword

Teaching comprehension strategies is a series of seven books using modelling, discussion and guided and independent practice to teach pupils strategies they can use to develop different reading comprehension skills.

Titles in this series include:

- *Teaching comprehension strategies—Book A*
- *Teaching comprehension strategies—Book B*
- *Teaching comprehension strategies—Book C*
- *Teaching comprehension strategies—Book D*
- *Teaching comprehension strategies—Book E*
- *Teaching comprehension strategies—Book F*
- *Teaching comprehension strategies—Book G*

Each book in this series is also provided in digital format on the accompanying CD.

Contents

What is comprehension?

Comprehension is a cognitive process. It involves the capacity of the mind to understand, using logic and reasoning. It is not, as some pupils sadly believe, trying to guess the answers to formal exercises, done with a pencil and paper, after reading text. Pupils need to know **how to think about and make decisions about a text after reading it**.

Teaching comprehension

Comprehension skills can and should be developed by teaching pupils strategies that are appropriate to a particular comprehension skill and then providing opportunities for them to discuss and practise applying those strategies to the texts they read. These strategies can be a series of clearly defined steps to follow.

Pupils need to understand that it is the **process** not the product that is more important. In other words, they need to understand **how** it is done before they are required to demonstrate that they can do it.

With higher order comprehension skills, care needs to be taken to ensure that the text is at an appropriate level and that the language of discussion is also age-appropriate.

The emphasis should be on discussion of: the text, thinking processes, activities and strategies that can be used to better comprehend text.

Many pupils will benefit from completing some of the comprehension activities orally before moving to supported and then independent pen and paper work.

Note: The terms *skills* and *strategies* are sometimes confused. The following explanation provides some clarification of how the two terms are used in this book.

Skills relate to competent performance and come from knowledge, practice and aptitude.

Strategies involve planning and tactics.

In other words, we can teach *strategies* that will help pupils to acquire specific comprehension *skills*.

Metacognitive strategies

Metacognitive strategies, teaching pupils how to think about thinking, are utilised in developing the twelve comprehension skills taught in this book. Metacognitive strategies are modelled and explained to pupils for each skill. As this is essentially an oral process, teachers are encouraged to elaborate on and discuss the explanations provided on the 'Learning about the skill' pages and to talk about different thought processes they would use in answering each question.

Pupils will require different levels of support before they are able to work independently to comprehend, make decisions about text and choose the best answer in multiple choice questions. This support includes modelling the metacognitive processes, as well as supported practice with some hints and clues provided.

Comprehension strategies

The exercises in this book have been written not to test, but to stimulate and challenge pupils and to help them to develop their thinking processes through modelled metacognitive strategies, discussion and guided and independent practice. There are no trick questions, but there are many that require and encourage pupils to use logic and reasoning.

Particularly in the higher order comprehension skills, there may be more than one acceptable answer. The reader's prior knowledge and experience will influence some of his or her decisions about the text. Teachers may choose to accept an answer if a pupil can justify and explain his or her choice. Therefore, some of the answers provided should not be considered prescriptive but more a guide and a basis for discussion.

There are pupils with excellent cognitive processing skills and a particular aptitude for and interest in reading who develop advanced reading comprehension skills independently. However, for the majority of pupils, the strategies they need to develop and demonstrate comprehension need to be made explicit and carefully taught, not just tested; the rationale behind this series of books.

Teachers notes

The following twelve comprehension skills are included in this book.

Understanding words	Sequencing	Concluding	Cause and effect
Finding information	Finding similarities and differences	Summarising	Fact or opinion
Identifying the main idea	Predicting	Inferring	Point of view and purpose

These twelve skills have been divided into four sections, each with teachers notes, three different comprehension skills and three pupil assessment tests.

Each group of six pages given to a particular skill consists of:

- Pupil page 1 — Text 1
- Pupil page 2 — Learning about the skill (teacher modelling of the skill)
- Pupil page 3 — Practice page (pupil practice with teacher assistance)
- Pupil page 4 — On your own (independent pupil activity)
- Pupil page 5 — Text 2
- Pupil page 6 — Try it out (independent pupil activity with one clue)

There is a test at the end of each section to assess the three skills, consisting of:

- Pupil page 1 — Text 3
- Pupil page 2 — Skill 1 test
- Pupil page 3 — Skill 2 test
- Pupil page 4 — Skill 3 test

A class test record sheet is provided on page viii and an individual pupil evaluation sheet is on page ix.

There are a variety of different text types used and identified in this book including:

Reports	Narratives	Discussions
Recounts	Procedures	Explanations

Teachers pages

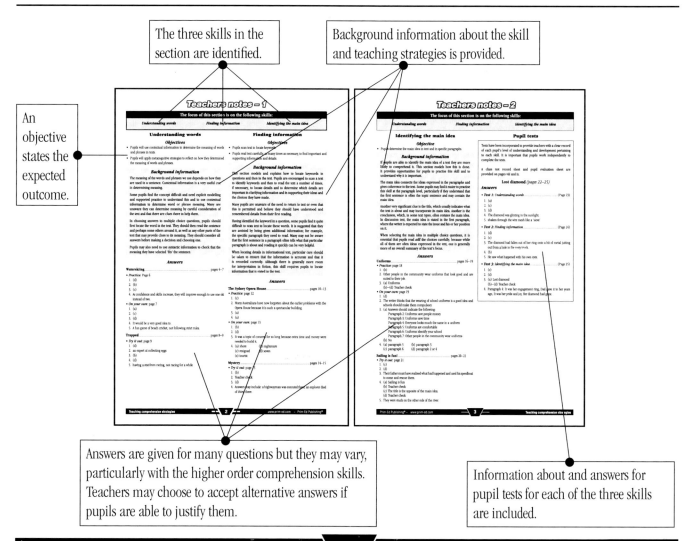

The three skills in the section are identified.

Background information about the skill and teaching strategies is provided.

An objective states the expected outcome.

Answers are given for many questions but they may vary, particularly with the higher order comprehension skills. Teachers may choose to accept alternative answers if pupils are able to justify them.

Information about and answers for pupil tests for each of the three skills are included.

Pupil pages

Text 1

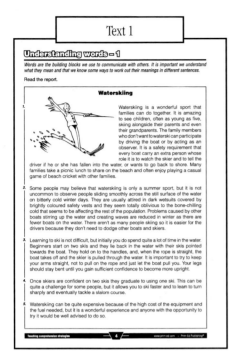

- The skill is identified and defined.
- The text is presented.

Learning about the skill

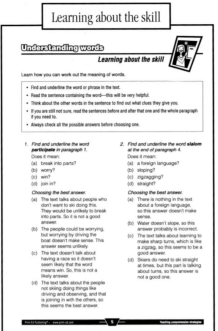

- The logo indicates that this is a teaching page.
- Steps and strategies are outlined.
- Multiple choice questions are presented and metacognitive processes for choosing the best answer are described.

Practice page

- The logo indicates that this is a teacher and pupil page.
- Some multiple choice questions and others requiring explanations are presented with prompts or clues to assist pupils.

On your own

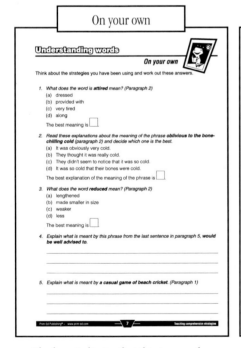

- The logo indicates that this is a pupil page.
- At least one multiple choice question and others requiring explanation are presented for pupils to complete.

Text 2

- The skill is identified.
- The text is presented.

Try it out

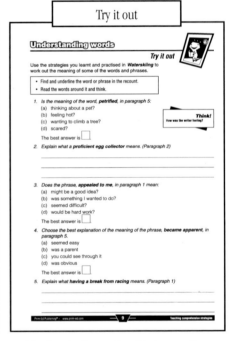

- The logo indicates that this is a pupil page.
- Multiple choice questions and some requiring explanation are included.

Pupil test pages

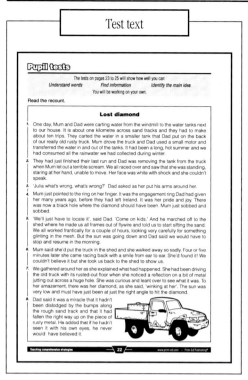

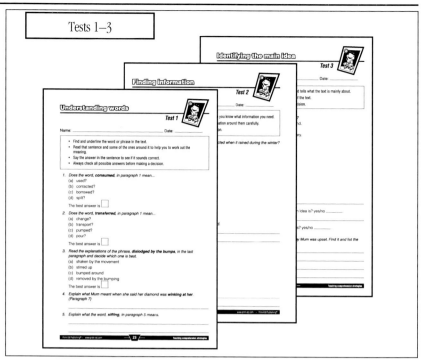

- The three skills to be tested are identified.
- The text is presented.

- Logo to indicate that this is a pupil page.
- The comprehension skill to be tested is identified and appropriate strategies and steps revised.
- Multiple choice questions and others requiring more explanation are presented.

Curriculum links

Country	Subject	Level	Objective
England	English	Year 4	• Identify themes and conventions. • Discuss words and phrases that capture the reader's interest and imagination. • Check that the text makes sense to them, discuss their understanding and explain the meaning of words in context. • Ask questions to improve their understanding of a text. • Draw inferences such as inferring characters' feelings, thoughts and motives from their actions, and justify inferences with evidence. • Predict what might happen from details stated and implied. • Identify main ideas from more than one paragraph and summarise these. • Identify how language, structure, and presentation contribute to meaning. • Retrieve and record information from non-fiction.
Northern Ireland	Language and Literacy	Year 5	• Participate in modelled, shared, paired and guided reading experiences. • Read, explore and understand a wide range of texts. • Justify their responses logically, by inference, deduction and/or reference to evidence within the text. • Use a variety of reading skills for different reading purposes.
Republic of Ireland	English	3rd Class	• Become an increasingly independent reader. • Experience different types of text. • Continue to develop a range of comprehension strategies. • Extend and develop his/her response to increasingly challenging reading material.
Scotland	Literacy and English	First	• Using what I know about the features of different types of texts, I can find, select, sort and use information for a specific purpose. • To show my understanding across different areas of learning, I can identify and consider the purpose and main ideas of a text. • To show my understanding, I can respond to different kinds of questions and other close reading tasks. • To help me develop an informed view, I can recognise the difference between fact and opinion. • I can share my thoughts about structure, characters and/or setting, recognise the writer's message and relate it to my own experiences, and comment on the effective choice of words and other features.
Wales	English	KS 2	• Read with increasing understanding. • Use inference, deduction and prediction to evaluate the texts they read and refer to relevant passages to support their opinions. • Adopt appropriate strategies; e.g. posing pertinent questions, identifying the precise information that they wish to know and distinguishing between fact and opinion.

Comprehension skills class test record

Name	Understanding words	Finding information	Identifying the main idea	Sequencing	Finding similarities and differences	Predicting	Concluding	Summarising	Inferring	Cause and effect	Fact or opinion	Point of view and purpose	Notes

Individual pupil evaluation

Name: _____

Skill	Strategies		Comments
Understanding words	knowledge ☺————————☹		
	application ☺————————☹		
Finding information	knowledge ☺————————☹		
	application ☺————————☹		
Identifying the main idea	knowledge ☺————————☹		
	application ☺————————☹		
Sequencing	knowledge ☺————————☹		
	application ☺————————☹		
Finding similarities and differences	knowledge ☺————————☹		
	application ☺————————☹		
Predicting	knowledge ☺————————☹		
	application ☺————————☹		
Concluding	knowledge ☺————————☹		
	application ☺————————☹		
Summarising	knowledge ☺————————☹		
	application ☺————————☹		
Inferring	knowledge ☺————————☹		
	application ☺————————☹		
Cause and effect	knowledge ☺————————☹		
	application ☺————————☹		
Fact or opinion	knowledge ☺————————☹		
	application ☺————————☹		
Point of view and purpose	knowledge ☺————————☹		
	application ☺————————☹		

The focus of this section is on the following skills:

Understanding words	*Finding information*	*Identifying the main idea*

Understanding words

Objectives

- Pupils will use contextual information to determine the meaning of words and phrases in texts.
- Pupils will apply metacognitive strategies to reflect on how they determined the meaning of words and phrases.

Background information

The meaning of the words and phrases we use depends on how they are used in a sentence. Contextual information is a very useful cue in determining meaning.

Some pupils find the concept difficult and need explicit modelling and supported practice to understand this and to use contextual information to determine word or phrase meaning. Many are unaware they can determine meaning by careful consideration of the text and that there are clues there to help them.

In choosing answers to multiple choice questions, pupils should first locate the word in the text. They should then read the sentence and perhaps some others around it, as well as any other parts of the text that may provide clues to its meaning. They should consider all answers before making a decision and choosing one.

Pupils may also need to use syntactic information to check that the meaning they have selected 'fits' the sentence.

Answers

Waterskiing..pages 4–7

- *Practice:* Page 6
  1. (d)
  2. (b)
  3. (c)
  4. As confidence and skills increase, they will improve enough to use one ski instead of two.
- *On your own:* page 7
  1. (a)
  2. (c)
  3. (d)
  4. It would be a very good idea to.
  5. A fun game of beach cricket, not following strict rules.

Trapped..pages 8–9

- *Try it out:* page 9
  1. (d)
  2. an expert at collecting eggs
  3. (b)
  4. (d)
  5. having a rest from racing, not racing for a while

Finding information

Objectives

- Pupils scan text to locate keywords.
- Pupils read text carefully, as many times as necessary, to find important and supporting information and details.

Background information

This section models and explains how to locate keywords in questions and then in the text. Pupils are encouraged to scan a text to identify keywords and then to read the text a number of times, if necessary, to locate details and to determine which details are important in clarifying information and in supporting their ideas and the choices they have made.

Many pupils are unaware of the need to return to text or even that this is permitted and believe they should have understood and remembered details from their first reading.

Having identified the keyword in a question, some pupils find it quite difficult to scan text to locate these words. It is suggested that they are assisted by being given additional information; for example, the specific paragraph they need to read. Many may not be aware that the first sentence in a paragraph often tells what that particular paragraph is about and reading it quickly can be very helpful.

When locating details in informational text, particular care should be taken to ensure that the information is accurate and that it is recorded correctly. Although there is generally more room for interpretation in fiction, this skill requires pupils to locate information that is stated in the text.

Answers

The Sydney Opera House..pages 10–13

- *Practice:* page 12
  1. (c)
  2. Many Australians have now forgotten about the earlier problems with the Opera House because it is such a spectacular building.
  3. (a)
  4. (a)
- *On your own:* page 13
  1. (b)
  2. (d)
  3. It was a topic of concern for so long because extra time and money were needed to build it.
  4. (a) shore   (b) nightmare
     (c) resigned   (d) seven
     (e) tourist

Mystery..pages 14–15

- *Try it out:* page 15
  1. (b)
  2. Teacher check
  3. (d)
  4. Answers may include: a highwayman was executed there; an explorer died of thirst there.

Teachers notes – 2

Identifying the main idea

Objective

- Pupils determine the main idea in text and in specific paragraphs.

Background information

If pupils are able to identify the main idea of a text they are more likely to comprehend it. This section models how this is done. It provides opportunities for pupils to practise this skill and to understand why it is important.

The main idea connects the ideas expressed in the paragraphs and gives coherence to the text. Some pupils may find it easier to practise this skill at the paragraph level, particularly if they understand that the first sentence is often the topic sentence and may contain the main idea.

Another very significant clue is the title, which usually indicates what the text is about and may incorporate its main idea. Another is the conclusion, which, in some text types, often restates the main idea. In discussion text, the main idea is stated in the first paragraph, where the writer is expected to state the issue and his or her position on it.

When selecting the main idea in multiple choice questions, it is essential that pupils read *all* the choices carefully, because while all of them are often ideas expressed in the text, one is generally more of an overall summary of the text's focus.

Answers

Uniforms...pages 16–19
- *Practice:* page 18
  1. (b)
  2. Other people in the community wear uniforms that look good and are suited to their job.
  3. (a) Uniforms
     (b)–(d) Teacher check
- *On your own:* page 19
  1. (d)
  2. The writer thinks that the wearing of school uniforms is a good idea and schools should make them compulsory.
  3. (a) Answers should indicate the following:
     Paragraph 2: Uniforms save people money
     Paragraph 3: Uniforms save time
     Paragraph 4: Everyone looks much the same in a uniform
     Paragraph 5: Uniforms are comfortable
     Paragraph 6: Uniforms identify your school
     Paragraph 7: Other people in the community wear uniforms
     (b) No
  4. (a) paragraph 5 (b) paragraph 3
     (c) paragraph 6 (d) paragraph 2 or 4

Sailing is fun!.. pages 20–21
- *Try it out:* page 21
  1. (c)
  2. (d)
  3. Their father must have realised what had happened and used his speedboat to come and rescue them.
  4. (a) Sailing is fun
     (b) Teacher check
     (c) The title is the opposite of the main idea.
     (d) Teacher check
  5. They were stuck on the other side of the river.

Pupil tests

Tests have been incorporated to provide teachers with a clear record of each pupil's level of understanding and development pertaining to each skill. It is important that pupils work independently to complete the tests.

A class test record sheet and pupil evaluation sheet are provided on pages viii and ix.

Lost diamond *(pages 22–25)*

Answers

- **Test 1:** *Understanding words*...(Page 23)
  1. (a)
  2. (c)
  3. (d)
  4. The diamond was glinting in the sunlight.
  5. shaken through the wire mesh like a 'sieve'

- **Test 2:** *Finding information*...(Page 24)
  1. (d)
  2. (c)
  3. The diamond had fallen out of her ring onto a bit of metal jutting out from a hole in the rusty truck.
  4. (b)
  5. He saw what happened with his own eyes.

- **Test 3:** *Identifying the main idea*...................................(Page 25)
  1. (c)
  2. (d)
  3. (a) Lost diamond
     (b)–(d) Teacher check
  4. Paragraph 4: It was her engagement ring, Dad gave it to her years ago, It was her pride and joy, Her diamond had gone.

Words are the building blocks we use to communicate with others. It is important we understand what they mean and that we know some ways to work out their meanings in different sentences.

Read the report.

Waterskiing

1. Waterskiing is a wonderful sport that families can do together. It is amazing to see children, often as young as five, skiing alongside their parents and even their grandparents. The family members who don't want to waterski can participate by driving the boat or by acting as an observer. It is a safety requirement that every boat carry an extra person whose role it is to watch the skier and to tell the driver if he or she has fallen into the water, or wants to go back to shore. Many families take a picnic lunch to share on the beach and often enjoy playing a casual game of beach cricket with other families.

2. Some people may believe that waterskiing is only a summer sport, but it is not uncommon to observe people sliding smoothly across the still surface of the water on bitterly cold winter days. They are usually attired in dark wetsuits covered by brightly coloured safety vests and they seem totally oblivious to the bone-chilling cold that seems to be affecting the rest of the population. Problems caused by other boats stirring up the water and creating waves are reduced in winter as there are fewer boats on the water. There aren't as many people skiing so it is easier for the drivers because they don't need to dodge other boats and skiers.

3. Learning to ski is not difficult, but initially you do spend quite a lot of time in the water. Beginners start on two skis and they lie back in the water with their skis pointed towards the boat. They hold on to the handles, and, when the rope is straight, the boat takes off and the skier is pulled through the water. It is important to try to keep your arms straight, not to pull on the rope and just let the boat pull you. Your legs should stay bent until you gain sufficient confidence to become more upright.

4. Once skiers are confident on two skis they graduate to using one ski. This can be quite a challenge for some people, but it allows you to ski faster and to learn to turn sharply and eventually tackle a slalom course.

5. Waterskiing can be quite expensive because of the high cost of the equipment and the fuel needed, but it is a wonderful experience and anyone with the opportunity to try it would be well advised to do so.

Understanding words

Learn how you can work out the meaning of words.

- Find and underline the word or phrase in the text.
- Read the sentence containing the word—this will be very helpful.
- Think about the other words in the sentence to find out what clues they give you.
- If you are still not sure, read the sentences before and after that one and the whole paragraph if you need to.
- Always check all the possible answers before choosing one.

1. Find and underline the word **participate** in paragraph 1.

   Does it mean:
   (a) break into parts?
   (b) worry?
   (c) win?
   (d) join in?

   Choosing the best answer.
   (a) The text talks about people who don't want to ski doing this. They would be unlikely to break into parts. So it is not a good answer.
   (b) The people could be worrying, but worrying by driving the boat doesn't make sense. This answer seems unlikely.
   (c) The text doesn't talk about having a race so it doesn't seem likely that the word means win. So, this is not a likely answer.
   (d) The text talks about the people not skiing doing things like driving and observing, and that is joining in with the others, so this seems the best answer.

2. Find and underline the word **slalom** at the end of paragraph 4.

   Does it mean:
   (a) a foreign language?
   (b) sloping?
   (c) zigzagging?
   (d) straight?

   Choosing the best answer.
   (a) There is nothing in the text about a foreign language, so this answer doesn't make sense.
   (b) Water doesn't slope, so this answer probably is incorrect.
   (c) The text talks about learning to make sharp turns, which is like a zigzag, so this seems to be a good answer.
   (d) Skiers do need to ski straight at times, but this part is talking about turns, so this answer is not a good one.

Understanding words

Use similar strategies to those on page 5 to practise working out word meanings. (Clues are given to help you.)

1. Find and underline the word **role** in paragraph 1.

   Does it mean:
   (a) something you can eat?
   (b) turning over and over?
   (c) watching?
   (d) work?

   The best answer is ☐.

   > **Think!**
   > Read the sentence, trying each of the answers in it and think about which one makes the most sense.

2. Find and underline the word **initially** in paragraph 3.

   Does it mean:
   (a) some letters?
   (b) at the beginning?
   (c) later?
   (d) before?

   The best answer is ☐.

   > **Think!**
   > The sentence will give you a clue and so will the next two sentences.

3. What does the word **observer** mean?

   (a) an object
   (b) the driver
   (c) someone who watches
   (d) someone who skis

   The best answer is ☐.

   > **Think!**
   > Read the sentence the word is in (paragraph 1) and the next sentence.

4. Explain what you think the phrase **graduate to using** means?

   _____

   _____

   _____

   > **Think!**
   > The beginning of the sentence in paragraph 4 will give you a very good clue.

Understanding words

Think about the strategies you have been using and work out these answers.

1. *What does the word is* **attired** *mean? (Paragraph 2)*
    (a) dressed
    (b) provided with
    (c) very tired
    (d) along

    The best meaning is ☐.

2. *Read these explanations about the meaning of the phrase* **oblivious to the bone-chilling cold** *(paragraph 2) and decide which one is the best.*
    (a) It was obviously very cold.
    (b) They thought it was really cold.
    (c) They didn't seem to notice that it was so cold.
    (d) It was so cold that their bones were cold.

    The best explanation of the meaning of the phrase is ☐.

3. *What does the word* **reduced** *mean? (Paragraph 2)*
    (a) lengthened
    (b) made smaller in size
    (c) weaker
    (d) less

    The best meaning is ☐.

4. *Explain what is meant by this phrase from the last sentence in paragraph 5,* **would be well advised to.**

    _____

    _____

    _____

5. *Explain what is meant by* **a casual game of beach cricket.** *(Paragraph 1)*

    _____

    _____

    _____

Read the recount.

Trapped

1. Last school holidays, my Aunty Shirley and Uncle Ron invited me to stay with them at their orchard. They needed help for two weeks while my cousin was away. I was very excited because they have quite a big orchard, cows, chickens, a tractor and a horse they are looking after while it has a break from racing. I have always lived in the city and working with animals, picking fruit and driving a tractor appealed to me enormously.

2. My first job was to collect the eggs. Some of the hens were reluctant to leave their eggs and my uncle had to show me how to persuade them to move. At first I was very hesitant, especially when the hens were facing me, but I soon became a very proficient egg collector.

3. During the afternoon I had my first driving lesson and then I drove Uncle Ron down to the orchard and helped to pick some fruit. It was an awesome experience, driving down the hill and over the small bridge that crossed their creek. I was amazed when Uncle Ron asked me to drive back to the shed by myself to get some more packing boxes. But I did it!

4. Tomorrow morning, Aunty Shirley is going to teach me how to milk a cow. They only milk two cows and they use the milk to drink and they make their own butter. It sounds quite complicated but I'm sure I will be able to do it with sufficient practice.

5. At about five o'clock, Uncle Ron asked me to collect the large container he puts the horse feed in. I marched into the empty stable, picked up the tin and turned around to leave. It suddenly seemed very dark in there. The reason very quickly became apparent. There, standing in the doorway, was the largest horse I had ever seen. There was no way I could get out. The horse just stood there, not coming in and not going away. I was *petrified*. I remember hearing somewhere that horses kick. All I could see were long, long legs and a huge head with enormous eyes that kept staring at me.

6. I tried saying 'go away' and 'go home' but it just stood there. Uncle Ron had gone up to the shed to organise the food, so there was no use yelling—he was too far away. I was trapped. My confidence evaporated and I felt a large tear trickle down my face. I had to do something, so I dropped the food container and edged my way towards the door, managing to squeeze past the horse. Then I ran all the way to the shed.

7. Uncle Ron listened to the story I blurted out as I tried to recover my breath. He was very patient but I think his lips were twitching as he explained how I could have got the horse to back up. That is one job I won't be volunteering to do again, not for some time.

Understanding words

Use the strategies you learnt and practised in **Waterskiing** to work out the meaning of some of the words and phrases.

> • Find and underline the word or phrase in the recount.
>
> • Read the words around it and think.

1. Is the meaning of the word, **petrified**, in paragraph 5:
    (a) thinking about a pet?
    (b) feeling hot?
    (c) wanting to climb a tree?
    (d) scared?

    The best answer is ☐.

> **Think!**
> How was the writer feeling?

2. Explain what a **proficient egg collector** means. (Paragraph 2)

    _____

    _____

    _____

3. Does the phrase, **appealed to me**, in paragraph 1 mean:
    (a) might be a good idea?
    (b) was something I wanted to do?
    (c) seemed difficult?
    (d) would be hard work?

    The best answer is ☐.

4. Choose the best explanation of the meaning of the phrase, **became apparent**, in paragraph 5.
    (a) seemed easy
    (b) was a parent
    (c) you could see through it
    (d) was obvious

    The best answer is ☐.

5. Explain what **having a break from racing** means. (Paragraph 1)

    _____

    _____

    _____

When you read text you can usually remember some of the information, but if you are asked about details you should read the text again to locate and check that your information is correct. Remember: The answer you are looking for is there in the text, you just need to find it!

Read the report.

The Sydney Opera House

1. This well-known Australian landmark is recognised throughout the world and is a leading tourist attraction. Set on the shore of Sydney Harbour, its soaring sails are visible from the city's other equally famous and widely recognised symbol, the Sydney Harbour Bridge.

2. In 1956, an international competition to design the opera house was won by the Danish architect, Joern Utzon. His daring and expensive design caused a great deal of controversy. His plan was criticised because many people didn't like his unusual design and doubted that it would work. It would be very different and look like no other building in the world.

3. Construction began in 1959 and delays and budget problems proved to be a nightmare for all concerned. It was finally completed in 1973. The original cost had been estimated at seven million dollars but the final cost was 102 million, even after some changes had been made to the original plans in an effort to save money. The government did not have the money needed to complete the building and extra money had to be raised by conducting special opera house lotteries. It was a topic of great concern and was discussed all around Australia for many years.

4. Utzon, tired of all the criticism, resigned in 1966 and left Australia. This was well before the building was complete. It was left to a group of Australian architects to redesign the interior and to try to reduce the cost. It took another seven years before it was finally finished. It was such a spectacular building that gradually many Australians forgot about all the problems and became proud of their opera house.

5. In 1999, the New South Wales government proposed some much needed renovations and invited Utzon to return to Australia and to act as a consultant. He was 81 years old and in all those years he had never returned to see his extraordinary achievement. It was a wonderful reconciliation after so long and it was no doubt an emotional experience for the man whose imagination and vision played such an important part in creating this amazing building.

Finding information

Learning about the skill

Learn how to find information in text.

- Read the question very carefully. Keywords in the question will tell you what information and details you need to find. Underline them.
- Think about your answer, but you will need to look at the text to check that you are correct.
- Find the keywords in the text and carefully read the information around them.
- Check all the possible answers before making a decision.

---

1. **Why was there controversy about the design of the Sydney Opera House?**
   - (a) People wanted an Australian to design it and didn't want a Dane to do it.
   - (b) The design wasn't new enough.
   - (c) People thought it would cost too much.
   - (d) They didn't like the unusual design and thought it wouldn't work.

   Choosing the best answer. The keywords are **controversy** *and* **design.**
   - (a) Although the designer was a Dane, the text does not say that this was a reason for the controversy. So this is not a good answer.
   - (b) The text says that the building would be like no other building in the world, so it would have to be a new design. This answer is not a good one.
   - (c) There was a problem with the cost of the building, but this is discussed later in the text and wasn't part of the original controversy. This answer could be a possibility.
   - (d) The text in this section actually says that people didn't like the unusual design and doubted that it would work, so this is the best answer.

2. **Why did Utzon leave Australia?**
   - (a) His contract was finished.
   - (b) There wasn't enough money to finish the building.
   - (c) He couldn't deal with all the criticism.
   - (d) He didn't think his design would work.

   Choosing the best answer. The keywords are **Utzon,** **leave** *and* **Australia.**
   - (a) The text does not mention his contract, so this answer is not a good one.
   - (b) There wasn't enough money to finish the building, but this isn't why he left.
   - (c) It says that he was tired of all the criticism and left Australia so this is a very good answer.
   - (d) It says that other people thought his plan wouldn't work, but it doesn't say that he thought this. So this is not a good answer.

Practice page

Use similar strategies to those on page 11 to find information.
(Clues are given to help you.)

1. *Why did they make changes to the original plans?*
   (a) People didn't like them.
   (b) There were so many delays.
   (c) They needed to save money.
   (d) Utzon didn't like them.

   The best answer is ☐.

   > **Think!**
   > One of the keywords is 'changes'. Look in paragraph 3 and read to the end of the sentence.

2. *Explain why many Australians have now forgotten about the earlier problems with the opera house.*

   _____

   _____

   _____

   _____

   > **Think!**
   > Look in paragraph 4 after you have decided on two keywords. Read the whole sentence.

3. *Why did Utzon return to Australia?*
   (a) He was invited to come.
   (b) He was getting old.
   (c) He loved Australia.
   (d) He thought it had been too long since his last visit.

   The best answer is ☐.

   > **Think!**
   > Look for keywords in paragraph 5.

4. *Extra money for the opera house was provided by:*
   (a) special lotteries
   (b) Utzon
   (c) the architects
   (d) donations

   The best answer is ☐.

   > **Think!**
   > Read paragraph 3 and look for keywords.

Finding information

Think about the strategies you have been using and work out these answers.

1. *What did the Australian architects do?*
    (a) Worked with Utzon.
    (b) They redesigned the interior.
    (c) Organised lotteries.
    (d) They told Utzon what to do.

    The best answer is ☐.

2. *How much did they originally estimate the opera house would cost?*
    (a) $102 000 000
    (b) 1 million dollars
    (c) 100 million dollars
    (d) 7 000 000 dollars

    The best answer is ☐.

3. *Explain why the opera house was a topic of concern in Australia for so long.*

    _____

    _____

    _____

4. *Find words from the text to complete these sentences.*

    (a) The Sydney Opera House is set on the _____ of Sydney's harbour.

    (b) Delays and budget problems were a _____ for the people concerned with the construction of the opera house.

    (c) In 1966, Utzon _____ and left Australia.

    (d) It took _____ years to complete the building after Utzon left Australia.

    (e) The Sydney Opera House is an important _____ attraction.

Read the narrative.

Mystery

1. 'Grandma you must know what the mystery is, I know you do, but why won't you tell me?'

2. Jake must have asked his grandparents this same question a million times, but they wouldn't tell him anything. They had lived there all their lives and they just had to know something about it, but why wouldn't they tell him? Whenever he asked, they seemed get a strange, almost frightened look on their faces. He was sure that it wasn't just his imagination.

3. The object of his concern was a big, old, ugly tree growing on the edge of the park. Children played around the other trees, but not this one. Older people sat on the benches under other trees, but not under this one. There always seemed to be lots of birds, but none flew around this tree. Even the bees and other insects seemed to stay away. There were no flowers growing around its trunk and it seemed a bit colder near the tree. A wind always blew, even on a still day, and the whistling noise made the hairs on the back of his neck stand up.

4. Jake did have a good imagination and he enjoyed writing mystery stories. His teacher said his stories were different, interesting and imaginative. But this was different, he felt it in his bones. Why couldn't he find someone who knew the answer?

5. Perhaps it is haunted. Did they execute a highwayman there many years ago? Did an alien spaceship land close to it? Did an early explorer die of thirst as he lay exhausted against its thick trunk? Was the tree planted many years ago by some really wicked person or did someone bury something evil beneath it?

6. Jake went to talk to his grandfather and to tell him some of these gruesome ideas. Perhaps his grandfather's reaction to one of his ideas would provide Jake with a clue.

7. They were sitting on the settee and his grandfather was listening intently to his ideas. Then his grandfather's eyes started to water, he threw his head back and made a funny gurgling sound in his throat. Jake was really startled, perhaps he was getting somewhere at long last. Then his grandfather bent forward and gasped out, 'Oh boy, but do you have an imagination'.

8. It was only then that Jake realised his Grandfather was doubled up with laughter, and he wandered off to think about some of the many other mysteries that were bothering him.

Finding information

Try it out

Use the strategies you learnt and practised in **The Sydney Opera House** to find information and details.

- Work out the keywords and find them in the text.
- Check all answers before you make a decision.

1. Did Jake's grandparents get a frightened look on their faces when they:

    (a) walked past the tree?

    (b) were asked questions about the tree?

    (c) told a story about the tree?

    (d) talked about the olden days?

    The best answer is ☐.

    > **Think!**
    > Find the keywords 'grandparents' and 'frightened' in paragraph 2.

2. Describe some of Jake's gruesome ideas.

    _____

    _____

    _____

    _____

    _____

3. What did grandfather do when he listened to Jake's ideas?

    (a) nodded his head

    (b) went to sleep

    (c) choked

    (d) started to laugh

    The best answer is ☐.

4. Explain why Jake was concerned about the tree.

    _____

    _____

    _____

    _____

Identifying the main idea – 1

If you know what the main idea of a text is, you will have a much better chance of understanding what it is about.

Read the discussion text.

Uniforms

1. School uniforms are a really good idea and I believe they should be worn by all pupils at every school. I find it difficult to understand why some pupils are so reluctant to wear their uniforms and why some schools do not make them compulsory.

2. Uniforms save people money. Because pupils wear the same thing everyday, parents don't need to buy so many different clothes. Some pupils want to wear designer jeans, shoes and tops, which look great, but are very expensive for parents to buy and quickly go out of fashion. Often they are made out of material that doesn't last long or wash well. Uniforms are made from very good fabric that lasts.

3. We always seem to be in a hurry in the mornings and we worry about being late for school and getting into trouble. It can take a lot of time to decide what to wear to school, whereas, it is much quicker and easier to just put on a uniform.

4. There are fewer differences between pupils in uniform. If their parents don't have a lot of money or don't want to spend their money on their children's clothes, it isn't so obvious. Also, it isn't as noticeable if pupils are thin or fat, because uniforms are usually less fitted than some clothes. There is not as much pressure on pupils to look good if everyone wears the same thing.

5. It is important for pupils to feel comfortable at school and to be able to move easily. Uniforms are designed more for comfort than style and are easy to wear.

6. Uniforms show that we go to a particular school. We should be proud of our school and our school's uniform.

7. School pupils are not the only people in the community who wear uniforms. Think about police officers, bus drivers, nursing staff and many others. They all wear uniforms. Their uniforms are suitable for the work they do and I think they look good too.

8. Pupils should understand all the advantages of school uniforms, be happy and wear them every day with pride.

Identifying the main idea

Learn how to work out the main idea and why it is important.

- There are many ideas in a text, but one idea is the link that joins the other ideas together—this is the main idea.

- Read the text then ask yourself, 'what is it mainly about'?
  (The title is a useful clue to the main idea because a good title often tells the reader what the text is about.)

- Always check all the answers before choosing one.

1. *The main idea of* 'Uniforms' *is:*
   (a) Uniforms save people money.
   (b) Lots of people wear uniforms.
   (c) Uniforms look good.
   (d) All pupils should wear uniforms.

   Choosing the best answer
   (a) The writer believes that uniforms save people money and this is the main idea of paragraph 2, but it is not the main idea of the text.
   (b) Lots of people do wear uniforms, but this is not what the text is mainly about.
   (c) The writer believes uniforms look good, but the text is not about how uniforms look. This is not the best answer.
   (d) The text is about uniforms being a good idea and it states that all pupils should wear them, so this is the best answer. This idea is stated in the first paragraph. The title also gives a good clue to the main idea of this text.

2. *The main idea of paragraph 3 is:*
   (a) Being late for school is a worry.
   (b) We always seem to be in a hurry before school.
   (c) It takes a lot of time to decide what to wear to school.
   (d) Uniforms save pupils' time.

   Choosing the best answer
   (a) It is a worry if you are late for school, but this is not the main idea the writer wants us to understand.
   (b) It does say that we always seem to be in a hurry in the morning, but it is not a paragraph about people being late. It is more about *why* we could be late.
   (c) If we don't wear a uniform it can take time to decide what to wear. This is a possible answer.
   (d) This is a better answer, because the paragraph is mainly about uniforms saving time and it gives a number of reasons for this.

Identifying the main idea

Use similar strategies to those on page 17 to practise finding the main idea. (Clues are given to help you.)

1. *What is the main idea in paragraph 2?*

   (a) Some of the clothes pupils like to wear to school are expensive.

   (b) School uniforms save people money.

   (c) School uniforms last longer.

   (d) Designer clothes look great.

   The best answer is ☐.

   > **Think!**
   > What are all the ideas in this paragraph about?

2. *Explain what paragraph 7 is mainly about.*

   _____

   _____

   _____

   _____

   > **Think!**
   > Think about the main idea and what the writer thinks about it.

3. *Answer these questions.*

   (a) What is the title of the text?

   _____

   > **Think!**
   > The title is important.

   (b) A good title often tells the main idea.

   Do you think this is a good title? _____

   (c) Explain why you think this.

   _____

   _____

   _____

   _____

   (d) Suggest another title that tells the main idea.

   _____

Identifying the main idea

Use the strategies you have been practising and work out these answers.

1. *What is the main idea of paragraph 4?*
   (a) Uniforms are less fitted than some clothes.
   (b) Thin pupils look better in school uniforms.
   (c) Some parents don't want to spend lots of money on clothes.
   (d) Pupils look the same in uniform.

   The best answer is ☐.

2. *The first paragraph tells what the writer thinks about the topic of school uniforms. Explain his or her opinion.*

   _____

   _____

   _____

3. (a) Write a very brief sentence to state the main idea in each paragraph.

   Para 2 _____

   Para 3 _____

   Para 4 _____

   Para 5 _____

   Para 6 _____

   Para 7 _____

   (b) Did all these paragraphs start with the main idea? _____

4. *Think about the main idea of each paragraph. Write the number of the paragraph where you think each of these comments belong.*

   (a) 'I can't run in these shoes.' ....☐

   (b) 'Haven't you decided what you're wearing to school yet?'....☐

   (c) 'Which school do you go to?'..................................☐

   (d) 'I can't afford to buy you that shirt, Tom.' ....☐

Read the narrative.

Sailing is fun

1. My big brother bought a small yacht and couldn't wait to get it into the water. He didn't have anyone better to go with him so he asked me. I'd never been sailing and I didn't have a clue what to do, but he told me that sailing is fun so I said I'd go.

2. We took the yacht down to the river and he tried to look as if he knew what he was doing. It took ages to organise the sails but finally we were on the water. But it wasn't long before we were both *in* the water. We swam over to the upturned yacht and he managed to pull it up, scramble on—and then it sailed off because he'd forgotten to release the sail. He went sailing past at quite a speed and yelled for me to grab hold and climb in. Fat chance of that! My hands banged against the sides as he flew past. We tried the same thing a number of times until I yelled for him to just stop and I would swim over and climb on.

3. I wish I could say that we sailed around and had a great time but that just didn't happen. He couldn't get the yacht to go where he wanted and we kept getting further and further away from the shore. Of course, where we were had to be the very widest part of the river. The opposite shore was getting closer and closer. When the water was quite shallow we decided to get out and we pulled the yacht into the beach. Finally, it was going in the direction we wanted!

4. We looked back to where we'd come from. It looked such a long way and the wind was blowing strongly towards us. We had no chance of sailing back. I was tired, wet and very grumpy. The water was murky and there was lots of weed in this part of the river. It wasn't a great place to be stuck. There weren't any houses nearby so we couldn't find anyone to help us and I could see us being stuck there all night.

5. My brother just stood there playing with the ropes on his yacht. He didn't have a thing to say and he obviously didn't have a clue about what we should or could do. I was so cross and worried; it was getting late and I was cold and miserable.

6. I noticed a small speedboat that seemed to be heading our way. I waved at it while my brother looked embarrassed. As it came closer, it looked familiar. Then I recognised Dad. I had never been so pleased to see anyone in my life!

Identifying the main idea

Try it out

Use the strategies you learnt and practised in **Uniforms** to find the main idea.

- The main idea links all the other ideas together and tells what the text is about.
- Look at the title too!
- Read the text and ask yourself, 'What is it mainly about?'
- Read all the possible answers carefully before making a decision.

1. What is the main idea of paragraph 2?
   - (a) The writer had trouble getting back on the yacht.
   - (b) They both fell in the water.
   - (c) Big brother wasn't a very good sailor.
   - (d) He forgot to release the sail.

   The best answer is ☐.

   > **Think!**
   > Which answer tells what it is mainly about and links all the ideas?

2. What is the main idea of the recount?
   - (a) Sailing is fun.
   - (b) Sailing is dangerous.
   - (c) Dad is a hero.
   - (d) Sailing isn't always fun.

   The best answer is ☐.

3. The main idea of the last paragraph is that they were rescued. Explain how this happened.

   _____

   _____

4. (a) What is the title? _____

   (b) Do you think it is a good title? _____

   (c) Explain how this title is connected to the main idea of the recount.

   _____

   (d) Suggest another appropriate title: _____

5. What is the main idea of paragraph 4?

   _____

The tests on pages 23 to 25 will show how well you can:

Understand words   Find information   Identify the main idea

You will be working on your own.

Read the recount.

Lost diamond

1. One day, Mum and Dad were carting water from the windmill to the water tanks next to our house. It is about one kilometre across sand tracks and they had to make about ten trips. They carted the water in a smaller tank that Dad put on the back of our really old rusty truck. Mum drove the truck and Dad used a small motor and transferred the water in and out of the tanks. It had been a long, hot summer and we had consumed all the rainwater we had collected during winter.

2. They had just finished their last run and Dad was removing the tank from the truck when Mum let out a terrible scream. We all raced over and saw that she was standing, staring at her hand, unable to move. Her face was white with shock and she couldn't speak.

3. 'Julia what's wrong, what's wrong?' Dad asked as her put his arms around her.

4. Mum just pointed to the ring on her finger. It was the engagement ring Dad had given her many years ago, before they had left Ireland. It was her pride and joy. There was now a black hole where the diamond should have been. Mum just sobbed and sobbed.

5. 'We'll just have to locate it', said Dad. 'Come on kids.' And he marched off to the shed where he made us all frames out of flywire and told us to start sifting the sand. We all worked frantically for a couple of hours, looking very carefully for something glinting in the mesh. But the sun was going down and Dad said we would have to stop and resume in the morning.

6. Mum said she'd put the truck in the shed and she walked away so sadly. Four or five minutes later she came racing back with a smile from ear to ear. She'd found it! We couldn't believe it but she took us back to the shed to show us.

7. We gathered around her as she explained what had happened. She had been driving the old truck with its rusted-out floor when she noticed a reflection on a bit of metal jutting out across a huge hole. She was curious and leant over to see what it was. To her amazement, there was her diamond, as she said, 'winking at her'. The sun was very low and must have just been at just the right angle to hit the diamond.

8. Dad said it was a miracle that it hadn't been dislodged by the bumps along the rough sand track and that it had fallen the right way up on the piece of rusty metal. He added that if he hadn't seen it with his own eyes, he never would have believed it.

Understanding words

Name: _____ Date: _____

- Find and underline the word or phrase in the text.
- Read that sentence and some of the ones around it to help you to work out the meaning.
- Say the answer in the sentence to see if it sounds correct.
- Always check all possible answers before making a decision.

---

1. *Does the word,* **consumed***, in paragraph 1 mean...*
   (a) used?
   (b) contacted?
   (c) borrowed?
   (d) spilt?

   The best answer is ☐.

2. *Does the word,* **transferred***, in paragraph 1 mean...*
   (a) change?
   (b) transport?
   (c) pumped?
   (d) pour?

   The best answer is ☐.

3. *Read the explanations of the phrase,* **dislodged by the bumps***, in the last paragraph and decide which one is best.*
   (a) shaken by the movement
   (b) stirred up
   (c) bumped around
   (d) removed by the bumping

   The best answer is ☐.

4. *Explain what Mum meant when she said her diamond was* **winking at her***. (Paragraph 7)*

   _____

   _____

5. *Explain what the word,* **sifting***, in paragraph 5 means.*

   _____

   _____

Name: _____ Date: _____

- Underline keywords in the question to make sure you know what information you need.
- Find the keywords in the text and read the information around them carefully.
- Always check all answers before making a decision.

---

1. *What had happened to all the water they collected when it rained during the winter?*
   (a) It was still in their tanks
   (b) They spilt it.
   (c) It disappeared.
   (d) They had used it all.

   The best answer is ☐.

2. *Why did Mum point to her finger?*
   (a) She had lost her ring.
   (b) She liked her ring.
   (c) The diamond had come out of her ring.
   (d) Her finger was sore.

   The best answer is ☐.

3. *Explain what had happened to Mum's diamond.*

   _____

   _____

4. *Why did Mum go to the shed?*
   (a) to look for her diamond
   (b) to put the truck away
   (c) to make a sifter
   (d) She wanted to be alone.

   The best answer is ☐.

5. *Why did Dad say he believed the story?*

   _____

   _____

Name: _____ Date: _____

- The main idea links all other ideas together and tells what the text is mainly about.
- The title is an excellent clue to the main idea of the text.
- Always check all answers before making a decision.

---

1. What is the main idea of the last paragraph?
   (a) The diamond hadn't fallen on the ground.
   (b) The diamond fell the right way up.
   (c) Dad thought it was an unbelievable story.
   (d) Dad didn't believe it really happened.

   The best answer is ⬚.

2. What is the main idea of the recount?
   (a) Mum loved her diamond ring.
   (b) Mum and Dad were carting water.
   (c) Sifting lots of sand.
   (d) Finding a diamond that had been lost.

   The best answer is ⬚.

3. (a) What is the title of the recount? _____

   (b) Do you think the title tells what the main idea is? yes/no _____.

   (c) Write another suitable title. _____

   (d) Does your title tell what the main idea is? yes/no _____.

4. The main idea in one paragraph is to tell why Mum was upset. Find it and list the reasons why she was so upset.

   _____

   _____

   _____

   _____

The focus of this section is on the following skills:

Sequencing	Finding similarities and differences	Predicting

Sequencing

Objective

- Pupils will sequence events.

Background information

This section demonstrates how to determine the order in which events occur, sometimes using time markers and other strategies to identify the relationship between events.

Knowing the sequence of events is an important, often critical, factor in a reader's understanding of a text.

Firstly, pupils need to determine from the question which events they are required to sequence. Then, they should locate them in the text and look for any time markers that could be helpful. Examples could include *before, then, when, while, after, finally, at last* or *following*.

Pupils may also find time lines of sections of the text or specific events a useful strategy.

Answers

Misery .... pages 28–31

- *Practice:* page 30
  1. (a)
  2. (d)
  3. He took it to show his brother.
  4. He pushed him over for the third time.
- *On your own:* page 31
  1. (d)
  2. (c)
  3. he left the field a mess and hurting all over, he didn't get any sympathy, he walked back to where his bike was to find it gone, he continued to walk all the way back home
  4. He lost patience with his brother and threw a ball at him which hit him in the face.

Planting seedlings .... pages 32–33

- *Try it out:* page 33
  1. (c)
  2. Box 1: Prepare the soil, Box 2: Dig holes, Box 3: Pour some water in each hole, Box 4: Remove seedlings from punnets
  3. You have to add soil if necessary to keep the seedlings the correct height.
  4. You need to keep the seedlings well watered and fertilise regularly, according to the instructions.

Finding similarities and differences

Objective

- Pupils will compare and contrast people, places and events.

Background information

The ability to compare and contrast the information provided in a text enhances the reader's understanding of that text and is an important comprehension skill pupils need to practise.

Pupils are required to categorise information to determine what some people, places and events have in common, or how they differ.

Graphic organisers are a very useful tool for identifying similarities and differences, particularly Venn diagrams, T–charts and compare and contrast charts.

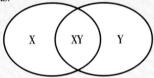

Venn diagram

same	different

T-chart

A	B	A	B
compare		contrast	

Compare and contrast chart

Answers

Favourite recipes .... pages 34–37

- *Practice:* page 36
  1. (b)
  2. (a) Diagram, teacher check. Sugar only: Cornflake biscuits, Chocolate bars, Apricots only: Almond biscuits, Both: Chocolate balls (b) No
  3. They both use coconut, butter and fruit.
  4. Teacher check, many possible answers.
- *On your own:* page 37
  1. (b)
  2. (d)
  3. (a) Chocolate balls and Almond biscuits (b) Both biscuits are refrigerated overnight, both are dipped in melted chocolate, both use apricots and chocolate.
  4. (a) vanilla, cocoa, icing sugar or hot water (b) sultanas and dates (c) flour, sugar, coconut or butter (d) They are both baked.

Frogs/Toads .... pages 38–39

- *Try it out:* page 39
  1. (c)
  2. (c)
  3. Frogs have long, strong hind legs and toads have short hind legs. Frogs use theirs for jumping and toads use theirs more for hopping.
  4. Frogs' eggs are laid in bunches, while toads' eggs are laid in long strings.
  5. Frogs jump away fast from their predators, while toads produce a toxic, unpleasant-tasting skin secretion so they are not good to eat.

The focus of this section is on the following skills:

| Sequencing | Finding similarities and differences | Predicting |

Predicting

Objective

- Pupils will use information from text to predict outcomes not explicitly stated in the text.

Background information

To be able to predict outcomes, often in terms of the probable actions or reactions of specific characters, pupils need to focus on content and to understand what they read. They need to monitor their understanding as they read, constantly confirming, rejecting or adjusting their predictions.

The focus of this section is on teaching pupils how to locate and use the information provided in the text to determine probable outcomes and then to evaluate their predictions.

Pupils need to be able to locate specific information related to an issue and/or characters, using keywords and concepts. Their predictions should not be wild guesses, but well thought out, logical ideas based on the information provided and some prior knowledge.

If pupils' answers differ, it is suggested that they check again to see why their answer varies from the one given. If they can justify their answer, teachers may decide to accept it.

Answers

The aviary..pages 40–43
- *Practice:* page 42
  1. Yes. Because he says in the third paragraph that he still believed the girls were silly and that little things like that couldn't hurt anyone.
  2. (b)
  3. (c)
  4. He was not worried about birds at a distance so he would feel fine.
- *On your own:* page 43
  1. (c)
  2. (c)
  3. Teacher check
  4. Teacher check

Rules..pages 44–45
- *Try it out:* page 45
  1. (d)
  2. (a)
  3. (c)
  4. Teacher check
  5. Teacher check

Pupil tests

Tests have been incorporated to provide teachers with a clear record of each pupil's level of understanding and development pertaining to each skill. It is important that pupils work independently to complete the tests.

A class test record sheet and pupil evaluation sheet are provided on pages viii and ix.

The Rocky Mountaineer *(pages 46–49)*

Answers

- **Test 1**: *Sequencing*...(Page 47)
  1. (d)
  2. (b)
  3. The train travels all day through some magnificent scenery to Kamloops, where passengers are transferred by coach to a hotel.
  4. (d)
  5. (c)

- **Test 2**: *Finding similarities and differences*.................(Page 48)
  1. (c)
  2. (a)

Activity Journey	1	2	3
Start in Vancouver	✓	✓	✓
Spend two days on the train	✓	✓	✗
Sleep in Kamloops	✓	✓	✗
Eat on the train	✓	✓	✓
Stay next to a beautiful lake	✓	✗	✗
Transfer to a hotel in a coach	✓	✗	✗
Visit Jasper	✓	✗	✓

  (b) Journey 1
  3. Journeys 1 and 3
  4. (a) Choose two of the following: start in Vancouver by rail, travel all day to Kamloops, spend night in Kamloops, leave by train next day, visit magnificent lake, can return to Vancouver by train, can continue journey by coach
  (b) In Journey 1, you end up in Jasper. In Journey 2, you end up in Banff.

- **Test 3**: *Predicting*...(Page 49)
  1. (c)
  2. (a)
  3. Teacher check
  4. Teacher check
  5. (c)

Sequencing – 1

If you want to understand what you read you must be to be able to work out the order in which events happen. This is called sequencing.

Read the recount.

Misery

1. Last Saturday was the worst day of my life. I've had bad days before, but nothing like this. By the time I climbed into bed I was battered and bruised and feeling so miserable, I just wanted to pull the quilt up over my head and cry like a baby.

2. My day started much too early, when my little brother came to show me his new kite. It would never fly again because the dog had tried to eat it. I stupidly said I had one somewhere that he could have. Of course, he wanted me to get up and find it and he stood there going on and on about it for hours. I lost patience and threw a ball. It hit him in the face and, naturally, his nose started to bleed.

3. Minutes later Mum was there yelling at me to get up and clean up the mess I'd caused. Then she said that I couldn't watch television for the whole weekend. Most of the blood was in my room and it was all over my football boots, socks, shirt and shorts which I'd piled up on the floor ready for today's game. I finally got them clean but they were soaking wet and I had to wear them that way. Yuk!

4. I went into the kitchen to have breakfast and my sister was just finishing the last of the cereal she knows I like and I really need. I had to have toast, which everyone knows it not enough for a footballer. I was so mad I dropped the jam and the jar smashed all over the floor. In came Mum again—and I get to clean up and put the rubbish out for a week!

5. Mum made me ride my bike about ten kilometres to football—no fun in wet gear! I was about halfway there when I realised that I had a flat tyre. There was no choice. I left my bike against a tree and I walked and ran the rest of the way.

6. I was late and the coach went ballistic. He sent me on, to mark Hercules's big brother. He was enormous! I was tired and fed up and when he pushed me over for the third time I stupidly decided to teach him a lesson.

7. The rest of the game was a disaster. When I left the field after my worst performance ever, I was a mess and I hurt all over. Everyone said it was my own fault because I'd started it and I didn't get any sympathy. Then I had to walk all the way home. Of course, when I reached the tree, my bike was gone.

8. After walking all the way I got home and Dad bellowed at me for being late and for losing my bike. He said he won't buy me another one and he sent me to my room without any dinner. I'm so miserable, I just want to cry.

Sequencing

Learning about the skill

Learn how you can work out the sequence of events.

Remember that the order in which things happen is very important.

- Make sure you understand which events you need to sequence.
- Look in the text to find the events listed as possible answers and underline them.
- You will need to work out how these events are related. There may be some time marker words such as *then*, *before* or *next* in the text to help you.
- Always check all possible answers before making a decision.

1. **Which event happened after his brother's nose started to bleed?**

   (a) He threw a ball at his brother.

   (b) His brother came into his room.

   (c) The dog ate the kite.

   (d) His mother yelled at him.

   Choosing the best answer.

   (a) The ball hit his brother on the nose before it started to bleed, so this is not the right answer.

   (b) His brother came into his room before his nose started to bleed, so this can't be the right answer.

   (c) The dog ate the kite before his brother came into the room, so this isn't the right answer.

   (d) His mother yelled at him because he made his brother's nose bleed. This is the right answer, because it happened after the nosebleed.

2. **What happened just before the jar of jam smashed on the floor?**

   (a) He went out of the kitchen.

   (b) His sister ate all the cereal.

   (c) He was cross with his sister.

   (d) Mum came into the kitchen.

   Choosing the best answer.

   (a) He smashed the jar while he was in the kitchen, so this can't be the right answer.

   (b) His sister ate the cereal and this made him cross. This must have happened before the jar was smashed. This could be the right answer, but did it happen *just* before?

   (c) He was cross after his sister ate the cereal, so this is a better answer than (b) and it is probably the right answer. Remember, you must check all the answers.

   (d) Mum came in after the jar smashed, so this is not the right answer.

Sequencing

Use similar strategies to those on page 29 to practise sequencing. (Clues are given to help you.)

1. *What happened first?*

   (a) The coach went ballistic.

   (b) The boy pushed him over again.

   (c) He was feeling tired and fed up.

   (d) He was a mess and hurt all over.

   The best answer is ☐.

> **Think!**
> You will need to find all of the answers in the text to work out which one happened first.

2. *Which one of these events should be listed as event number 3 below?*

   (a) He wanted to cry.

   (b) He didn't get any dinner.

   (c) His bike was gone.

   (d) His dad said he wouldn't get him a new bike.

> **Think!**
> Read events 1, 2 and 4 first, then try to work out which event is missing.

> Event 1. He walked home.
> Event 2. Dad bellowed at him.
> Event 3.
> Event 4. Dad sent him to his room.
>
> Event number 3 is_____.

3. *What did his little brother do straight after the dog ate his kite?*

   _____

   _____

   _____

> **Think!**
> You will need to read paragraph 2 and think about this one.

4. *What happened just before he decided to teach Hercules's big brother a lesson?*

   _____

   _____

> **Think!**
> Read paragraph 6 to find the answer.

On your own

Think about the strategies you have been using and work out these answers.

1. What happened after he left his bike?
    (a) He had a flat tyre.
    (b) He was halfway to football.
    (c) He rode his bike.
    (d) He walked and ran to football.

    The best answer is ☐.

2. What happened first?
    (a) He washed his football clothes.
    (b) He put them on.
    (c) His clothes were on the floor.
    (d) He had breakfast.

    The best answer is ☐.

3. Write all the things that happened after he decided to teach the boy he was marking a lesson and before he got home.

    _____

    _____

    _____

    _____

4. Explain what happened between these two events.
    • His little brother was carrying on.
    • His brother's nose started to bleed.

    _____

    _____

    _____

Read the procedure.

Planting seedlings

Read these directions explaining how to plant punnets of seedlings successfully in a garden.

- Choose a suitable position in the garden. Some plants prefer sunlight while others grow better in a shady position. The instructions provided with the seedlings should give you this information.

- Water the seedlings so they will not be stressed before transplanting.

- Try to plant the seedlings later in the day to avoid midday heat.

- Prepare the soil by adding fertiliser and turning it over.

- Dig appropriately spaced holes and pour some water in each hole.

- Remove seedlings gently by pushing up on the bottom of the punnet.

- Place a seedling beside each hole, trying to keep the original soil around the roots.

- Place seedlings in holes, adding soil if necessary to keep the seedlings at the correct height.

- Fill holes with soil and press down firmly to remove any air spaces.

- Water lightly.

- Keep seedlings well watered and fertilise regularly according to the instructions.

Sequencing

Try it out

Use the strategies you learnt and practised in **Misery** to work out the sequence of the instructions.

- Make sure you know which events you need to sequence.
- Find them in the text and underline them.
- Work out how they are related.
- Check all possible answers before making a decision.

---

1. *What should you do first?*

   (a) Turn over the soil.

   (b) Remove seedling from the punnet.

   (c) Choose a good position for seedlings.

   (d) Place seedlings beside holes.

   The best answer is ☐.

> **Think!**
> Find all the instructions in the text and work out which one comes first.

2. *Write the instructions in the correct boxes to show the sequence.*

   - Prepare the soil
   - Pour some water in each hole
   - Dig holes
   - Remove seedlings from punnets

1.	2.	3.	4.

3. *Explain the next thing you have to do after placing the seedlings in the holes.*

   _____

   _____

   _____

4. *What is the last thing you need to do?*

   _____

   _____

   _____

Finding similarities and differences – 1

To help you understand what you read in text, you sometimes need to think about how things are alike or how they are different and make comparisons.

Read the procedures.

Favourite recipes

My grandmother makes some delicious biscuits that we all enjoy. When we visit her, she cooks them especially for us. We all have our favourites. I asked her to write out my favourite four because I want to try to make them for my friends and myself.

Chocolate bars

1 cup plain flour
$\frac{1}{2}$ cup sugar
1 cup coconut
1 tbspn cocoa
200 g butter
$\frac{1}{2}$ tspn vanilla

Icing

1 cup icing sugar
30 g butter
2 tbspn cocoa
$1\frac{1}{2}$ tbspn hot water

Bake in moderate oven for 20 minutes. Cool and add icing.

Chocolate balls

125 g chocolate
12 marshmallows
110 g can reduced cream
$\frac{1}{2}$ cup sugar
1 tbspn orange juice
60 g glace apricots

Dipping chocolate

125 g chocolate
15 g coconut butter

Refrigerate balls overnight before dipping in melted chocolate and coconut butter.

Almond biscuits

250 g butternut biscuits
90 g toasted flaked almonds
$\frac{1}{4}$ cup coconut
60 g dried apricots
60 g butter
$\frac{1}{4}$ cup golden syrup
90 g chocolate
30 g extra flaked almonds

Refrigerate balls overnight and dip tops in melted chocolate. Decorate with extra toasted flaked almonds.

Cornflake biscuits

5 cups cornflakes
1 cup self-raising flour
1 cup coconut
$\frac{1}{2}$ cup brown sugar
1 cup dates
1 cup sultanas
200 g butter
2 eggs

Bake in moderate oven for 10 minutes/or until golden brown.

Finding similarities and differences

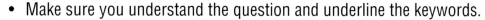

Learning about the skill

Learn how you can organise information to make it easier to answer questions about similarities and differences.

- Make sure you understand the question and underline the keywords.

- Sometimes it is easy to see how things are different or the same if you are comparing two things. However, if there are three or more things to compare, it can be helpful to organise the information in a chart. Two examples are shown below.

- Always check all the possible answers before making a decision.

---

1. *Which two recipes are baked?*

   (a) Chocolate balls and chocolate bars
   (b) Almond biscuits and chocolate balls
   (c) Chocolate balls and cornflake biscuits
   (d) Chocolate bars and cornflake biscuits

Baked	Unbaked

   Choosing the best answer.

   You will find it helpful to write each recipe in a column in the chart above.

   (a) Chocolate balls are not baked and chocolate bars are. Not the right answer.
   (b) Almond biscuits are not baked, nor are chocolate balls. Not the right answer.
   (c) Chocolate balls are not baked, but cornflake biscuits are. Not the right answer.
   (d) Chocolate bars are baked and so are cornflake biscuits. The right answer.

2. *Which recipe has butter and eggs?*

   Use the Venn diagram to help you to answer this question.

   (a) chocolate bars
   (b) chocolate balls
   (c) almond biscuits
   (d) cornflake biscuits

   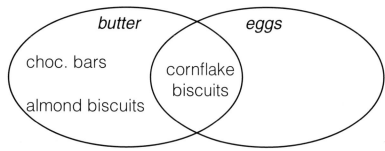

   Choosing the best answer.

   If you look at the Venn diagram you can see that there are two biscuits, (a) chocolate bars and (c) almond biscuits, which have butter and are in the butter only section. There are no biscuits in the eggs only section. There is only one biscuit, (d) cornflake biscuits, in the eggs section and also in the butter section. So (d), cornflake biscuits, is the right answer. They have both butter and eggs.

Finding similarities and differences

Practice page

Use similar strategies like those on page 35 to practise finding similarities and differences.

(Clues are given to help you.)

1. *Which recipe has both sugar and apricots?*

    Complete the chart to help answer this question.

    (a) chocolate bars

    (b) chocolate balls

    (c) almond biscuits

    (d) cornflake biscuits

    The best answer is ☐ .

sugar	apricots

2. (a) Use a Venn diagram to show the information you found to answer question 1.

    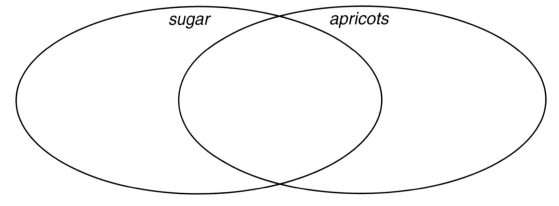

    (b) Is there a recipe that is not on your Venn diagram? _____

3. *What are three similarities between almond and cornflake biscuits?*

    _____

    _____

    _____

    > **Hint:**
    > You may be able to complete questions 3 and 4 without making a chart.

4. *What are two ways that almond and cornflake biscuits are different?*

    _____

    _____

Finding similarities and differences

On your own

Think about the strategies you have been using and work out these answers.

1. How are almond and cornflake biscuits the same?

   (a) They have sultanas in them.

   (b) They are made with butter.

   (c) They contain chocolate.

   (d) They have apricots.

   The best answer is ☐.

2. Which sentence is not true because chocolate bars and chocolate balls are different?

   (a) They are both made with sugar.

   (b) Chocolate or cocoa are ingredients.

   (c) They both need cooling before a chocolate coating is added.

   (d) They both contain cream.

   The best answer is ☐.

3. (a) There are two biscuits that do not need to be cooked. They are

   _____ and _____

   (b) Explain what else they have in common.

   _____

   _____

4. Answer the questions about the information shown on the Venn diagram.

   chocolate bars   cornflake biscuits

   vanilla   flour   eggs
   cocoa   coconut   sultanas
   icing sugar   butter   dates
   hot water   baked   cornflakes
                    sugar

   (a) Name two ingredients in chocolate bars that are not in cornflake biscuits.

   _____ and _____

   (b) Which two fruits are in cornflake biscuits? _____

   (c) Name two ingredients that are in both recipes.

   _____ and _____

   (d) There is something else that these biscuits have in common that is not an

   ingredient. What is it? _____

Finding similarities and differences – 2

Read the reports.

Frogs

1. Frogs are amphibians, which means they have two life stages: one they spend in water as tadpoles and the other is a semi-aquatic, adult stage. They belong to the *Ranidae* family of which there are more than 400 species. Frogs are found on every continent except Antarctica.

2. A moist environment is preferred by frogs. They have quite smooth and slimy skin. Their eyes tend to bulge and they have tiny teeth. They have four legs and they use their long, strong hind legs and webbed feet for swimming and for jumping away fast from their predators.

3. Frogs are able to vocalise, even underwater. The male attracts the female's attention in this way. They tend to lay eggs in ponds and ditches because there are no fish there to eat them. Their eggs are laid in bunches, a bit like grapes, and they hatch in about ten days. The tadpoles eat aquatic plants and algae, gradually changing into froglets. They then eat insects and grow quickly.

4. A group of frogs is called an army of frogs.

Toads

1. Toads are amphibians and belong to the *Bufonidae* family. There are more than 300 different species found naturally throughout the world, except in polar regions, Madagascar, Australasia and Polynesia. However, the cane toad, *Bufo marinus*, was introduced into some South Pacific islands and Australasia, where it is now causing huge problems.

2. Toads have dry, warty skin and most of them live on land. They have short, stubby bodies with short hind legs and even shorter front legs. They hop rather than jump and they are often not fast enough to escape their enemies, so they defend themselves by producing toxic, unpleasant-tasting skin secretions. This means they are not good to eat. Their eggs and tadpoles are also toxic.

3. To breed, toads need to return to water and when the males find a suitable place they call to the females. Their eggs look like long strings of black beads held together with a jelly-like substance. The tadpoles, which are smaller and darker than frog tadpoles, hatch within a few days, gradually changing into toadlets. They feed on insects and grow quickly.

4. A group of toads is called a knot of toads.

Finding similarities and differences

Try it out

Use the strategies you learnt and practised in **Favourite recipes** to work out similarities and differences.

> • Make sure you understand the question and underline the keywords.
> • Use a chart or a Venn diagram if you need it.
> • Always check all possible answers before making a decision.

1. Frogs and toads are the same because they:
   - (a) have smooth skin.
   - (b) can jump well.
   - (c) can lay eggs.
   - (d) belong to the *Bufonidae* family.

   The best answer is ☐.

   Think!
   Try to find each answer in both parts of the text.

2. What is the same about frog and toad legs?
   - (a) They are long.
   - (b) They are strong.
   - (c) There are four of them.
   - (d) They are suitable for jumping.

   The best answer is ☐.

3. What are two differences between frog and toad legs?

   _____

   _____

4. Describe how the eggs of frogs and toads are different.

   _____

   _____

5. What is different about the way frogs and toads avoid their predators?

   _____

   _____

   _____

As we read, it is important to think about what is happening and to work out what we think will happen next.

Read the narrative.

The aviary

1. Justin was terrified of birds. He didn't know why they frightened him so much, they just did. If a bird came anywhere near him, his hands would shake, his head would feel light and dizzy, his heart would pound and his legs would wobble.

2. Birds in the distance were fine and even close up in a cage was all right, as long as he didn't have to look too closely at their beady little eyes. He could talk about birds and the different species he read about on the Internet were fascinating, as long as they kept their distance.

3. Boys aren't supposed to be frightened of birds and he felt ashamed and as stupid as some of the girls at school who screamed when he tried to show them a live spider or a mouse. Why did they carry on like that? His teacher had noticed their reaction and had tried to explain to him that he needed to be more understanding, but he still believed that the girls were silly and that little things like that couldn't hurt anyone.

4. Justin had managed to keep his secret successfully until his class was going on an excursion to a wildlife park. Their teacher told them about one of its well-known features, a huge aviary you could walk through and where tame birds would come close and you could feed them. He was so worried that he told his best friend, Sam, who confessed that he felt the same way about snakes.

5. What could he do? His mother never let him stay home from school unless he was actually dying. Perhaps he could try, but she was hard to fool. He didn't seem to have any choice, he'd have to go. Perhaps he could try keeping his eyes closed or walking around the edge or just running through the middle very fast.

6. The dreaded day arrived and it was fun until they reached the aviary. Justin was terrified that if he went in he would collapse in a heap and make a fool of himself. He let the other pupils and teachers all go in and he was standing outside the gate when he felt his teacher's hand on his arm.

7. His teacher looked at him for a few seconds and then asked him if he would mind helping him to carry the lunches from the buses to the picnic area. Justin couldn't believe his good luck.

Predicting

Learn how to work out what probably happens next.

- The answers are not in the text, so you can't just read them, but there is information for you to use and think about.
- You need to find information related to the question. (This could be underlined.)
- Think hard! What is the writer suggesting might happen?
- Always consider all possible answers before making a decision.

---

1. *What do you think Justin will do next?*
   - (a) Run fast through the aviary.
   - (b) Ask his teacher to go through with him.
   - (c) Cry
   - (d) Help his teacher to carry the lunches.

   Choosing the best answer.
   - (a) Justin did think about running through the aviary if he had to go in. He doesn't have to do this now, so this is not a good answer.
   - (b) He could ask his teacher to go with him, but he would still be near the birds. This is probably not the best answer.
   - (c) Justin was very worried, but it doesn't say anything about crying in the text. This is not the best answer.
   - (d) Justin definitely did not want to go into the aviary. This answer is the only one that means he will not have to do this, so it is the best answer.

2. *What do you think would have happened if Justin had gone into the aviary?*
   - (a) He would have screamed.
   - (b) He would have run through very fast.
   - (c) He would have been very frightened.
   - (d) His friends would have made fun of him.

   Choosing the best answer.
   - (a) It did say that he would be scared, but nothing about him screaming. This is probably not the right answer.
   - (b) He did think about running fast, but this would be hard to do if his legs were shaking and he felt dizzy. This is probably not the best answer.
   - (c) Justin said that he was dreading going into the aviary and that he was terrified of birds, so this is a very good answer.
   - (d) Justin made fun of the girls when they were frightened, but it doesn't say anything about them making fun of him. This is not the best answer.

Predicting

Use similar strategies to those on page 41 to help you predict what will happen. (Clues are given to help you.)

1. *Do you think Justin will show the girls live creatures again?* _____

   Explain why you think this.

   _____

   _____

   _____

   _____

> **Think!**
> Read the last sentence in paragraph 3.

2. *Next time Justin's class goes to a place where there are birds, what do you think will happen?*
   (a) He won't be so scared.
   (b) He will tell his teacher that he is scared and ask for help.
   (c) He will ask his mum if he can stay at home.
   (d) He will close his eyes and run through the birds.

   The best answer is ☐.

> **Think!**
> What was the reason the trip worked out well for Justin?

3. *What would have happened if Justin hadn't told his friend, Sam, about his fear?*
   (a) He would have been more worried.
   (b) He would have told his mum.
   (c) His teacher wouldn't have known about it and helped him.
   (d) He would have been okay.

   The best answer is ☐.

> **Think!**
> How could his teacher have found out about his fear?

4. *Explain what you think Justin would feel if he saw a picture of a bird on the Internet?*

   _____

   _____

   _____

> **Think!**
> Read paragraph 2.

Predicting

Think about the strategies you have learnt and work out these answers.

1. *What would happen to Justin if he stood outside a cage with birds in it?*
    (a) His legs would go all wobbly.
    (b) He would want to scream.
    (c) He wouldn't look at their eyes.
    (d) He would run away.

    The best answer is ☐.

2. *What would happen if Sam saw a snake?*
    (a) He would run away.
    (b) He would tell his teacher.
    (c) He would feel very frightened.
    (d) He would think it was very interesting.

    The best answer is ☐.

3. *Do you think his teacher will talk to Justin later about his fear of birds?* _____

    Explain why you think this.

    _____

    _____

    _____

4. *Complete the sentence.*

    I think Justin will now think that his teacher is

    _____

    _____

    because

    _____

    _____

    _____

Read the narrative.

Rules

1. It was a beautiful spring day and Adam and Joel decided to take their motorbikes out for a ride around the farm. It was Adam's family's farm and he and his cousin had been having a wonderful time together. Today they wanted to explore the hilly back country in the far corner of the property, where they hadn't been before.

2. There were some very strict family rules about bike riding: things like helmets, protective clothing, places to go, speeds and communication. The boys didn't like them, but they knew they had to follow the rules.

3. Adam's dad watched them getting ready to go and his eagle eyes didn't miss a thing. Joel's helmet strap wasn't done up properly and Dad then wanted to check that Adam was wearing the right boots. He also made sure they had enough water and some fruit in their backpacks.

4. The boys had a great time zooming along the tracks and found some things they could jump over, but it was very hot work. When they reached the lake, they decided to have a swim and cool off.

5. As they scrambled out of the lake and looked at their backpacks and all the gear they needed to wear, they groaned. They knew they'd be coming back this way and could pick it up then.

6. It felt wonderful to have the wind blowing their hair and cooling their skin as they flew over the rough ground, whistling and yelling to each other. They were having the best time.

7. As they got into the hilly country they noticed lots of stones, some quite big ones, and lots of holes in the limestone. Joel moved back a bit after Adam's bike kicked up some stones and one hit his head just above his left eye. He was all right but it hurt like mad and he hoped it wasn't bleeding.

8. Up ahead, Adam stopped suddenly and dropped his bike. He'd hit a pothole and couldn't hold his bike up. He started yelling and it took Joel a while to realise that the hot exhaust pipe was on his leg. Joel raced up to help and managed to shift the bike, but the skin on Adam's leg was red and he was in a lot of pain.

9. Joel started to panic! What could he do? How stupid had they been?

Predicting

Use the strategies you learnt and practised in *The aviary* to make predictions.

- You need to find and underline information related to the question.
- The answer is not in the text, but there is information you can use and think about.
- The writer will suggest rather than tell what is likely to happen.

---

1. *What do you think Dad would have done if the boys didn't have the right gear when they left the farm?*

    (a) Told them that it was important.

    (b) Said that it didn't matter.

    (c) Told them to remember the rules next time.

    (d) Said that they couldn't go.

    The best answer is ☐.

> **Think!**
> Read paragraph 2 and think about the meaning of the word 'strict' and what Dad did in paragraph 3.

2. *What do you think the boys would need most after the accident?*

    (a) water

    (b) their helmets

    (c) their boots

    (d) some fruit

    The best answer is ☐.

3. *What do you think the boys' opinion of Dad and his rules is now?*

    (a) The rules are a waste of time.

    (b) Dad is too fussy.

    (c) The rules help to keep people safe.

    (d) There should be more rules.

    The best answer is ☐.

4. *Explain how you think wearing their gear would have helped the boys.*

    _____

    _____

    _____

5. *Do you think the boys will follow the rules next time they go riding?* _____

    Explain your answer.

    _____

    _____

    _____

Read the report.

The Rocky Mountaineer

1. The Rocky Mountaineer is a passenger train that travels through the spectacular, snow-tipped Canadian Rocky Mountains in late spring, summer and early autumn. People from all around the world are rushing to enjoy this unique rail journey.

2. Three of the different journeys available to passengers are described below.

3. The first leaves from Vancouver on the west coast and travels through some magnificent scenery to the small railway town of Kamloops. This non-stop journey takes a whole day and passengers do not reach Kamloops until early evening. They are transferred by coach to a hotel for the evening. Because of limited accommodation in the town, some are taken by coach to nearby mountain resorts. The following day their train continues, arriving that evening in Jasper, a tourist destination situated in the mountains beside a beautiful lake. Travellers have the option of continuing their journey the next day by coach or returning to Vancouver by train.

4. The second rail journey starts in Vancouver early in the morning and follows the same route, arriving in the early evening in Kamloops, where the passengers are accommodated for the night. They depart early and spend all day travelling to the world-renowned town of Banff, situated in the mountains near a swiftly flowing river where whitewater rafting is popular. The hot springs in Banff and the ski resorts close by make it a popular tourist destination all year round. It is not far from some magnificent lakes, one of the most famous being Lake Louise. Some passengers choose to return by train to Vancouver, but most extend their holiday, continuing to explore the Rocky Mountains by coach.

5. The Rocky Mountaineer is so popular that it introduced a third train journey in 2005. This leaves from Vancouver and takes a more northerly route through the famous ski resort of Whistler. Passengers have a choice of continuing in the train to Kamloops and then either Jasper or Banff, or they can return to Vancouver. This shorter journey was introduced for those tourists who wanted to experience the Rocky Mountains but had limited time.

6. Passengers who travel on the Rocky Mountaineer have the opportunity to see some breathtaking scenery, stay at some world famous hotels and enjoy some wonderful food and service on the train.

Sequencing

Name: _____ Date: _____

> • Make sure you know which events you need to sequence.
>
> • Find them in the text and underline them.
>
> • Work out how they are related.
>
> • Check all possible answers before making a decision.

1. *Where does Journey 2 go after leaving Kamloops?*

   (a) Vancouver

   (b) Whistler

   (c) Jasper

   (d) Banff

   The best answer is ☐.

2. *Where does Journey 3 go before reaching Kamloops?*

   (a) Jasper

   (b) Whistler

   (c) Banff

   (d) Lake Louise

   The best answer is ☐.

3. *Explain what happens on Journey 1 between these two events.*

   • The train leaves Vancouver.

   • The passengers go to bed that night.

   _____

   _____

   _____

   _____

4. *What do most travellers do after they arrive in Banff?*

   (a) Catch the train to Jasper

   (b) Return to Vancouver on the train

   (c) Return to Vancouver in a coach

   (d) Explore the Rocky Mountains

   The best answer is ☐.

5. *What would the passengers on Journey 2 do first?*

   (a) Spend all day on the train

   (b) Arrive in Kamloops

   (c) Leave Vancouver

   (d) Arrive in Banff

   The best answer is ☐.

Finding similarities and differences

Name: _____ Date: _____

> • Make sure you understand the question and underline the keywords.
> • Use a chart or a Venn diagram if you need it.
> • Always check all possible answers before making a decision.

1. *Which is one difference between Journeys 2 and 3?*

   (a) Goes to Kamloops.

   (b) Starts in Vancouver

   (c) Goes to Whistler

   (d) Travels through mountains

   The best answer is ☐.

2. (a) Use the chart to show similarities and differences. Tick the things the passengers on each journey can do.

Activity Journey	1	2	3
Start in Vancouver			
Spend two days on the train			
Sleep in Kamloops			
Eat on the train			
Stay next to a beautiful lake			
Transfer to a hotel in a coach			
Visit Jasper			

   (b) The passengers on Journey _____ can do all of the activities on the chart.

3. *Which journeys are shown on the Venn diagram?*

Journey _____

Finishes in Jasper
Goes to Kamloops

Leaves from Vancouver
Can return to Vancouver

Journey _____

Visits Whistler
Can visit Banff
Can visit Jasper
Can go to Kamloops

4. (a) What are two similarities between Journey 1 and 2?

   _____

   _____

   (b) What is the main difference between Journey 1 and Journey 2?

   _____

   _____

Name: _____ Date: _____

> • You need to find and underline information related to the question.
>
> • The answer is not in the text, but there is information you can use and think about.
>
> • The writer will suggest rather than tell what is likely to happen.
>
> • Always check all possible answers before making a decision.

1. *How do you think travellers would be feeling when they reach Kamloops?*
   - (a) very happy
   - (b) sad
   - (c) tired
   - (d) cross

   The best answer is ☐.

2. *Do you think the number of tourists going on the Rocky Mountaineer will:*
   - (a) increase?
   - (b) decease?
   - (c) stay the same?

   The best answer is ☐.

3. (a) Do you think the Rocky Mountaineer will ever travel in winter? _____

   (b) Explain. _____

   _____

4. (a) Would you want to take a camera on the Rocky Mountaineer? _____

   (b) Give reasons. _____

   _____

5. *How would the people who want to ski in winter get up into the Rocky Mountains?*
   - (a) train
   - (b) jet aircraft
   - (c) bus or car
   - (d) bicycle

   The best answer is ☐.

The focus of this section is on the following skills:

Concluding	Summarising	Inferring

Concluding

Objective

- Pupils will make judgments and reach conclusions based on facts and details provided in text.

Background information

This section demonstrates how to decide on the meaning of facts and details provided in text and to build up evidence in order to make judgments and reach conclusions about this information.

Pupils also need to be able to search for evidence to support a particular conclusion by locating the relevant information in the text and then making judgments about it.

In higher order comprehension skills such as this, answers are not always immediately obvious and discussion about why one answer is judged to be the best should be encouraged. However, teachers may decide to accept another answer, if a pupil can provide the necessary evidence to support the answer he or she has given.

Answers

The Taj Mahal .... pages 52–55

- *Practice:* page 54
  1. (c)
  2. Because people, materials and semi-precious stones from all over the world were purchased or had to be paid, which would have been extremely costly.
  3. (b)
  4. (b)
- *On your own:* page 55
  1. (b)
  2. (a)
  3. Teacher check
  4. Teacher check

The world's most boring game .... pages 56–57

- *Try it out:* page 57
  1. (c)
  2. (a)
  3. The writer's dad is sometimes tired and grumpy because he sits up late at night watching the cricket on television. He is also especially grumpy when his team/country isn't doing so well.
  4. Teacher check

Summarising

Objective

- Pupils will summarise text by linking important information and identifying the main points.

Background information

To be able to summarise text successfully, pupils first need to be clear about what they are being asked to do and the form their answer should take. (For example, a one-word answer or a more detailed explanation may be required.) It will help if they underline the critical words in the question.

They then need to locate any relevant information in the text, underline it and establish how it is linked. Words like while, but, and, when and as may be significant in establishing how the information is linked. Unnecessary and irrelevant information should be omitted and the main points established for inclusion in the summary.

Pupils may need to locate information throughout the entire text in order to summarise the main points for some questions.

Answers may vary and will require teacher checking. Those given below are provided as a guide to the main points.

Answers

Marie Antoinette .... pages 58–61

- *Practice:* page 60
  1. (c)
  2. When they married, Louis was shy and awkward. Marie was only 14 and didn't speak French very well.
  3. (a) lavish, expensive   (b) Teacher check
  4. (a) hungry, angry   (b) Teacher check
- *On your own:* page 61
  1. (a)
  2. (d)
  3. Because they declared war on France, she and Louis were arrested for treason and guillotined.
  4. The French people were hungry and attacked the palace because they believed all the grain was there.
  5. Teacher check

Whale sharks .... pages 62–63

- *Try it out*: page 63
  1. (d)
  2. (c)
  3. A whale shark's mouth is at the front and not the underside, it is a filter feeder, it moves its whole body and not just the tail and it is gentle.
  4. Possible answers: gentle, friendly, curious, huge, filter feeder, popular, harmless, wonderful.

The focus of this section is on the following skills:

Concluding	Summarising	Inferring

Inferring

Objective

- Pupils will make inferences about what is most likely to be true, based on information provided in the text.

Background information

Inferences are opinions about what is most likely to be true and are formed after careful evaluation of all the available facts. Pupils need to realise that because there is no information that tells them the actual answer, their inferences may not be correct. They need to determine what makes the most sense, given the information provided, and to then look for details to support their decisions.

The focus of this section is on teaching pupils how to use contextual information, both written and visual, to determine what they believe to be true, and then to find further evidence to support their decisions.

Pupil answers will need to be teacher checked, but some possible answers have been provided as a guide.

Answers

Stuck in the sand .... pages 64–67

- *Practice:* page 66
  1. (b)
  2. The vehicle was really stuck and ropes weren't strong enough.
  3. The vehicle was down deep into the sand, the tide was coming in and the sea breeze was blowing.
  4. It could lift the vehicle up and it had a heavier chain.
- *On your own:* page 67
  1. (b)
  2. (a)
  3. Dad took a long time to back the trailer down to the shore, the waves were moving the boat around and it was difficult to hold it, Dad wound the winch up slowly.
  4. (a) Yes
     (b) Mum was the one who suggested taking the boat off the trailer to make it the load lighter, she also took the advice of the man walking along the beach and organised the front-end loader.

Favourite sports .... pages 68–69

- *Try it out:* page 69
  1. (b)
  2. (d)
  3. (c)
  4. These are both played in competitions with other schools.

Pupil tests

Tests have been incorporated to provide teachers with a clear record of each pupil's level of understanding and development pertaining to each skill. It is important that pupils work independently to complete the tests.

A class test record sheet and pupil evaluation sheet are provided on pages viii and ix.

Our earthquake *(pages 70–73)*

Answers

- **Test 1**: *Concluding* .... (Page 71)
  1. (b)
  2. (a)
  3. He concluded his dad had the worst time because big cracks appeared on the tenth floor of the hospital where he worked and they had to get the patients out.
  4. (a) No
     (b) The school was on a hill and a few kilometres away from the beach.

- **Test 2**: *Summarising* .... (Page 72)
  1. (c)
  2. (a) frightened
     (b) Teacher check
  3. Answers should include picking up fallen items, discussing the earthquake with Miss Green and commencing a recount about their experiences.
  4. Answers should include that the writer thought Sam was playing around as usual, making the table shake and causing his or her pens to roll off.

- **Test 3**: *Inferring* .... (Page 73)
  1. (c)
  2. (a)
  3. Teacher check
  4. They needed to finish it at home because part of the recount was to tell what had happened to their families, pets and homes and they wouldn't know this until they got home.

Concluding – 1

Conclusions are decisions we make by working something out. We make conclusions about what we read by finding facts and details in the text and deciding what they mean.

Read the report.

The Taj Mahal

1. The beautiful Taj Mahal was built at Agra, India, in 1631. It is the country's pride and joy. The Taj Mahal is considered to be one of the seven wonders of the world.

2. The stunning white marble building took 20 000 people 22 years to construct. Building materials for the project were collected from all over India and other surrounding countries. A team of 1000 elephants was needed to transport them to the site. Architects, builders and artists from all over Asia and Europe worked on the building.

3. The Taj Mahal is a tomb. It was built by Shah Jahan as a symbol of his eternal love for his wife, Mumtaz Mahal. She died after the birth of their fourteenth child while they were away on a military campaign. It is recorded that Shah Jahan's beard and hair went snowy white within just a few months of his wife's death.

4. The white marble of the Taj Mahal is inlaid with thousands of semi-precious stones. It changes colour and appears pink in the morning, white in the evening and gold in the moonlight. There is a large garden surrounding the building and four reflecting pools that enhance its beauty.

5. Shah Jahan, who later became weak and depressed, was deposed by his son and spent eight years as a prisoner in the Great Red Fort. He was able to see the Taj Mahal from his prison, and when he died, he too was buried there.

6. The Taj Mahal is one of the most popular tourist attractions in the world and the millions of visitors are causing some concerns. They have even worn away some of the marble by walking through the building. Vehicle fumes from the city of Agra have damaged the building so much that a few years ago it needed to be cleaned.

7. It isn't surprising that so many people want to enjoy the exceptional beauty of this spectacular building and it is considered a national treasure and one of the wonders of the world.

Concluding

Learn how you can work out conclusions.

> Conclusions are decisions you make about the meaning of facts and details in the text.
>
> • Make sure you understand what it is you are making conclusions about.
> • Look in the text to find the facts and details and underline them.
> • You will need to make decisions about what they mean.
> • Always check all possible answers before making a decision.

1. Why did Shah Jahan build the Taj Mahal?

   (a) He was feeling sad.

   (b) He loved his wife.

   (c) He wanted India to have a beautiful building.

   (d) He wanted to show people how much he still loved his wife.

Choosing the best answer.

   (a) He was sad when his wife died, but this doesn't explain why he built it. This is not a really good answer.

   (b) It is true that he did love his wife, but this does not explain why he built it. Not the best answer.

   (c) He did make a beautiful building, but this doesn't explain why he built it. Not the best answer.

   (d) The text said that it was a symbol of his eternal love for his wife, which means that he wanted to show people that he still loved her. This is the best answer.

2. You can conclude that his hair and beard turned white because:

   (a) He was old.

   (b) He stopped dyeing it.

   (c) He was very affected and shocked by his wife's death.

   (d) He had to work so hard to build the Taj Mahal.

Choosing the best answer.

   (a) The detail in the text tells us that this happened in just a few months, so this can't be the correct answer.

   (b) Although it is possible that he dyed his hair, there is no information about it in the text, so this is not a good answer.

   (c) His wife died suddenly so he would have been shocked and he was affected by her death. This is a good answer.

   (d) He did work hard organising the building, but that took 22 years and his hair changed in a few months, so this is not a good answer.

Concluding

Use strategies similar to those on page 53 to practise making conclusions. (Clues are given to help you.)

1. You can conclude that Shah Jahan's wife is buried in the Taj Mahal because:

    (a) It was built after she died.

    (b) It is a beautiful building.

    (c) The text says that it is a tomb.

    (d) Shah Jahan loved her.

    The best answer is ☐.

    > **Think!**
    > The word 'buried' in the question is important.

2. You can conclude that the Taj Mahal was very expensive to build because:

    _____

    _____

    _____

    _____

    > **Think!**
    > Read paragraphs 2 and 4 and think about all the things that cost money.

3. Look in the text to find which of these words describes the Taj Mahal.

    (a) surprising

    (b) spectacular

    (c) attractive

    (d) wonderful

    The best answer is ☐.

    > **Think!**
    > Look for the words in paragraph 7.

4. What tells you that Agra is a very busy city today?

    (a) It is in India.

    (b) Car fumes from there damaged the Taj Mahal.

    (c) There are lots of people there.

    (d) All cities are busy.

    The best answer is ☐.

    > **Think!**
    > There is information to help you make this conclusion in paragraph 6.

Concluding

Think about the strategies you have been using and work out these answers.

1. *The Taj Mahal changes colour because:*
   (a) There is a large garden around it.
   (b) Semi-precious stones reflect the light.
   (c) There are reflecting pools around it.
   (d) There are different coloured lights on it.

   The best answer is ☐.

2. *You can conclude that the Great Red Fort was close to the Taj Mahal because:*
   (a) Shah Jahan could see the Taj Mahal when he was a prisoner.
   (b) They needed a fort to protect the Taj Mahal.
   (c) They needed lots of soldiers in Agra.
   (d) They are both in Agra.

   The best answer is ☐.

3. (a) Do you think that the Indian government wants people to visit the Taj Mahal?

   ☐ yes ☐ no

   (b) Give some reasons to support your conclusion.

   _____

   _____

   _____

4. (a) Would you like to visit the Taj Mahal?

   ☐ yes ☐ no

   (b) Explain why you reached this conclusion.

   _____

   _____

   _____

Read the discussion text.

The world's most boring game

1. The game of cricket is without a doubt more boring than watching grass grow. I suppose there are a few people who actually want to play the game and I guess they should be allowed to, but why does everyone else have to suffer? What I want is to have this game banned on both radio and television.

2. We only have one television in our house, so we can't escape cricket and we see nothing else for days and days. Then, if we go out in the car, we have to listen to it on the radio! When the cricket is on, all the usual programmes people enjoy watching disappear and we have to watch and listen to cricket for hours and hours and nothing ever happens. Even the news is full of cricket and the men who play it. I know that women play it too, but thank goodness it isn't broadcast.

3. Some games take five days to play and, after all that time, often there isn't a winner. The umpires don't seem to be able to make a decision and when something does happen, everything stops while they waste time looking at a replay. They can't play cricket in the rain and they waste time leaving the pitch while the covers are put on. When this happens, instead of showing something else, we have to listen to the commentators dribbling on about the seagulls on the ground.

4. They do play one day games which would be an improvement, if they played them *instead* of five day games, not *as well as*. A shorter, new 20–20 game has been introduced, but they have added that too, so it is no help at all.

5. When test matches are played overseas many people sit up half the night watching them. Surely this is very dangerous, because they are tired and could have an accident. I know my dad gets really tired and grumpy, especially when we are not doing too well. The very worst of the lot is the Ashes series, five matches, each five days long. Everyone gets so upset about it and no matter who wins, the Ashes actually stay at Lords in England.

6. Cricket must have a bad effect on work. So many people try to sneak a television into work or a radio and many, like my dad, waste time checking up on the Internet all the time. It can't be good for business.

7. It really is time that we all let people know how we feel and we must insist that we get our lives back again.

Concluding

Use the strategies you learnt and practised in **The Taj Mahal** to make conclusions.

> - Make sure you understand the question and what you are making conclusions about.
> - Look in the text for facts and details and underline them.
> - Decide what they mean.
> - Check all possible answers before making a decision.

1. **What is the writer's main purpose for writing this?**

   (a) To have cricket banned

   (b) To tell how he or she feels

   (c) To stop cricket being broadcast

   (d) To get another television set

   The best answer is ☐.

2. **What can you conclude about the writer's dad?**

   (a) He really loves cricket.

   (b) He wants to buy another television.

   (c) He works hard.

   (d) He enjoys driving.

   The best answer is ☐.

3. **Explain why the writer's dad is sometimes tired and grumpy.**

   _____

   _____

   _____

4. **Do you think the writer:**

   (a) hates cricket; or (b) is cross because it's on television all the time? ☐

   Explain why you reached this conclusion.

   _____

   _____

Summarising – 1

Summarising is giving the main ideas and facts without using many words. We need to link the important ideas and decide which are the main points.

Read the biography.

Marie Antoinette

1. Maria Antonia, born in 1755, was the beautiful daughter of the emperor of Austria. Austria and France had been fighting for many years and it was hoped that her marriage to the future king of France would bring peace and stability to Europe.

2. In 1770, the emperor sent his daughter to France, where she was immediately married to Louis, the king's grandson. He was a shy, awkward young man and Maria was only fourteen and didn't even speak French very well. If the French people were going to accept her she had to become 'more French' so they changed her name to Marie Antoinette. Four years later, the king died and Louis and Marie Antoinette became the king and queen of France.

3. Although there was great poverty in France, the king's court was lavish and expensive. Many of the people were hungry and they became very angry with the rich and powerful people because they didn't care about their problems.

4. Marie Antoinette enjoyed wearing beautiful clothes and jewellery and didn't know that the people were hungry. Later, she realised there was a problem and tried to save money, but the people didn't know this. It is believed that when she was told that people didn't have enough money to buy bread, her reply was, 'Let them eat cake'. She probably didn't make this famous comment, but everyone thought she did.

5. In 1785, she was blamed for what was known as the diamond necklace affair.

A trickster called Jeanne de la Motte persuaded Cardinal de Rohan that Marie Antoinette wanted him to buy her a necklace with 647 diamonds. He bought it and gave it to Jeanne to give to the queen, but Jeanne stole it and sent her husband to England to sell all the diamonds. After Jeanne was caught, the jeweller couldn't get any money to pay for the necklace he'd made. Because he expected Marie Antoinette to pay him, people believed she really wanted it.

6. When the situation became dangerous, Marie Antoinette was packed and ready to flee but Louis wouldn't go, so she stayed at Versailles with him. There were rumours that they were hoarding all the grain and the hungry people marched to Versailles and attacked the palace.

7. Later, when the king and queen tried to escape, they were captured and taken to Paris. Marie Antoinette appealed to Austria and Prussia for help and they declared war on France. This made matters worse for them and led to their arrest for treason. Louis was guillotined in January 1793, and Marie Antoinette in October.

Summarising

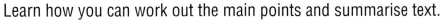

Learn how you can work out the main points and summarise text.
- Make sure you understand the question and underline keywords.
- Look for information in the text, decide what is important and how it is connected.
- Omit any unnecessary or unconnected information.
- Always check all the possible answers before making a decision.

1. **Which sentence would you leave out of a summary of reasons Marie Antoinette was disliked?**

   (a) She wore expensive clothes and jewellery.

   (b) She came from Austria.

   (c) The people thought she didn't care about them.

   (d) She was beautiful.

   Choosing the best answer.

   (a) When they didn't even have enough money for food, this would be an important reason and needs to be in the summary.

   (b) She was Austrian and France had been at war with Austria. This is important and should be in the summary.

   (c) She didn't know about the people's problems, so she didn't help them. They didn't understand this. It is important and needs to be in the summary.

   (d) She was beautiful but this wasn't connected to why they disliked her. This is the best answer, because it should not be in the summary.

2. **Which sentence best summarises why people believed Marie Antoinette said 'Let them eat cake'?**

   (a) They knew she liked cake.

   (b) They thought she didn't like bread.

   (c) They believed that she didn't know that cake cost more than bread, so she could have said it.

   (d) They thought she was making fun of them.

   Choosing the best answer

   (a) They knew she liked cake, but this didn't have anything to do with why they believed she said it. Not a good answer.

   (b) They didn't know what she thought about bread, so this is not a good answer.

   (c) They thought the person who said this had no idea about the cost of food. It was the kind of silly comment someone who didn't know they were hungry and had no money would make. A good answer.

   (d) There is no information about her being cruel or making fun of them. It is more about the fact that she didn't understand or care about their problems, so this is not the best answer.

Summarising

Use similar strategies to those on page 59 to practise summarising. (Clues are given to help you.)

1. Which sentence best summarises why the people were angry?

    (a) They didn't like Marie Antoinette.

    (b) Austria had been at war with France and she was Austrian.

    (c) They didn't have enough food and the court wasted money.

    (d) Marie Antoinette wore expensive clothes and jewellery.

    The best answer is ☐.

> **Think!**
> All of the sentences are true but which one summarises the main points best?

2. Summarise what would have made the marriage of Marie Antoinette and Louis difficult when they were first married.

    _____

    _____

    _____

> **Think!**
> You will find the main points for your summary in paragraph 2.

3. (a) Find two words in the text to summarise and describe the court of Louis and Marie Antoinette.

    • _____

    • _____

    (b) Write one word to summarise your opinion of Marie Antoinette.

    _____

> **Think!**
> Read paragraph 3 for two words to describe the court and two words to describe how the French people felt.

4. (a) Find two words in the text that best summarise the feelings of the people of France at this time.

    • _____

    • _____

    (b) Write one word to summarise your opinion of these French people.

    _____

Summarising

Think about the strategies you have been using and work out these answers.

1. Which sentence summarises the reason Marie Antoinette didn't leave Versailles?

   (a) Her husband wouldn't leave.

   (b) She wasn't ready in time.

   (c) She was too frightened.

   (d) She didn't have anywhere to go.

   The best answer is ☐.

2. How could Marie Antoinette's attitude towards the people of France be summarised?

   (a) She hated them.

   (b) She was frightened of them.

   (c) She was worried about them.

   (d) She didn't understand their problems.

   The best answer is ☐.

3. Summarise what happened when Marie Antoinette appealed to other countries for help for herself and her family.

   _____

   _____

   _____

4. Make a summary of the reasons why the French people attacked the Palace of Versailles.

   _____

   _____

   _____

5. Write a short summary about the story of the necklace. Do not include any unnecessary information.

   _____

   _____

Read the report.

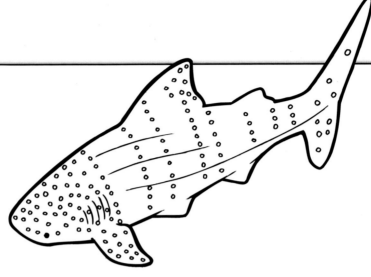

Whale sharks

1. The whale shark is a shark, not a whale. This huge, gentle creature is the world's largest fish. It is very popular with divers and snorkellers because it swims slowly at only about five kilometres per hour, quite close to the surface, and people can swim with them. They are harmless animals and seem quite friendly. They often seem even curious about the people who join them in the water.

2. Larger whale sharks grow to a length of 14 metres and weigh about 15 tonnes. The females, like most sharks, are bigger than the males. They have very thick grey skin with light yellow markings of stripes and dots. There are three long ridges on the upper side along each side of its body. They have a wide flat head and small eyes. The top fin of their tail is much larger than the lower one.

3. Unlike other sharks, the whale shark's huge mouth is located at the front and not on the underside of its head. It has about 3000 tiny teeth but it is a filter feeder and uses spongy filters to retain the plankton, tiny crustaceans and small fish, like sardines and anchovies, in the water it takes into its mouth.

4. The warm waters in tropical and subtropical oceans are home to whale sharks. They usually swim alone, moving their whole body from side to side, instead of just moving their tail as other sharks do.

5. Female whale sharks give birth to hundreds of pups about 60 cm long. They take about thirty years to mature and live from 100 to 150 years.

6. In recent years, whale sharks have become a great tourist attraction and thousands of people every year are lucky enough to watch and even swim with them when they are close to the shore. However, it is important to remember that these wonderful creatures are a treasure we must value and protect.

Summarising

Try it out

Use the strategies you learnt and practised in **Marie Antoinette** to summarise information.

- Make sure you understand the question and underline keywords.
- Decide what information is important and how it is connected.
- Omit any unnecessary or unconnected information.
- Always check all the possible answers before making a decision.

1. Which sentence summarises why whale sharks are popular with snorkellers and divers?

   (a) They are harmless.

   (b) They stay close to the surface.

   (c) They swim slowly.

   (d) Divers and snorkellers can swim with the whale sharks.

   The best answer is ☐.

   > ***Think!***
   > Which sentence connects the ideas?

2. Which sentence best summarises why whale sharks are not dangerous?

   (a) They have about 3000 small teeth.

   (b) They stay near the surface and move slowly.

   (c) They are gentle creatures and are filter feeders.

   (d) They are very slow moving.

   The best answer is ☐.

3. Summarise the differences between whale sharks and other sharks.

   _____

   _____

   _____

   _____

4. Choose six words from the text that you think really summarise whale sharks.

   _____   _____

   _____   _____

   _____   _____

Inferring – 1

When we read we often make decisions about what we think is most likely to be true, based on the information given in the text. This is called inferring.

Read the narrative.

Stuck in the sand

1. It had been a long, hot morning for Ben and his parents. They had been fishing in the bay and had a bucketful of herring and a few whiting, but the sea breeze was in and the water was becoming quite choppy.

2. Dad ran their boat onto the sand and climbed out. He rubbed his knees as he walked slowly towards the four-wheel drive he had parked on the beach. Mum and Ben held onto the boat and waited for him to return. The waves were moving the boat around and it took all their strength to stop the water washing it onto the shore.

3. It seemed ages before Dad returned, backed the trailer into the water and released the cable used to pull the boat onto the trailer. Ben grabbed the end of the cable and attached it to the boat. His dad wouldn't let him use the winch so he and Mum steadied the boat as Dad slowly winched it up and onto the trailer.

4. When the boat was secure, Dad climbed into the vehicle, started the engine and put it into gear. He revved the engine hard; the wheels of the four-wheel drive turned and turned, but the boat didn't go anywhere. Mum yelled and waved at Dad to stop and finally he turned the ignition off and came back to look. The front wheels had broken through the sand into the thick seaweed below and had dug in. Mum yelled that we needed to take the boat off the trailer to make it lighter. We tried that, but the four-wheel drive was really stuck.

5. Three other four-wheel drivers who tried to help broke their tow ropes. The vehicle didn't budge—it was really stuck. The tide was coming in and the waves were actually washing in the driver's window.

6. Mum left Ben to struggle with the boat and stood on the beach, holding her head. A local man walking past with his dog spoke to her, then Ben and Dad watched her racing off up the beach and along the road.

7. Mum came back about five minutes later, followed by a front-end loader. The driver attached a chain to the vehicle, but that snapped too. He left and returned with another, thicker chain that even three men had difficulty moving. Eventually, he lifted the vehicle up and pulled it out of the water.

Learn how to work out what is most likely to be true.

- The answers are usually not in the text, but there is information given that will give you clues to think about. (This could be underlined.)
- Find the answer that makes the most sense and is supported by text details.
- Always consider all possible answers before making a decision.

---

1. **How do you think Ben and his parents were feeling when they got back from their fishing trip?**

   (a) seasick

   (b) cold and tired

   (c) hot and unhappy

   (d) tired and happy

   Choosing the best answer.

   (a) The water was choppy, but it doesn't say anything that would suggest that they were seasick because of it. This is probably not the best answer.

   (b) It had been a long morning and they could have been tired, but it was a hot day. This is probably not the best answer.

   (c) They were possibly feeling hot but they had caught lots of fish, so they were probably not unhappy. This is not the best answer.

   (d) They had a long morning, so they were probably tired and they had caught lots of fish, so they were probably happy. This is the best answer.

2. **Why did Mum race off up the beach?**

   (a) She couldn't stand watching what was happening.

   (b) She needed to go to the shop.

   (c) She was going to find the man with the front-end loader.

   (d) She was really worried.

   Choosing the best answer.

   (a) Mum was holding her head, so she was probably very worried, but this doesn't explain why she raced away. This is probably not the best answer.

   (b) There is nothing in the text to suggest she wanted to go to the shop. This is not a good answer.

   (c) Mum did come back followed by the front-end loader, so this is a very good answer.

   (d) Mum held her head, which probably meant she was worried and what was happening was very worrying, but this doesn't explain why she raced off. Not the best answer.

Use similar strategies to those on page 65 to help you decide what you think is most likely to be true based on information from the text. (Clues are given to help you.)

1. How do you think Mum knew about the man with the front-end loader?

    (a) Dad told her.

    (b) The local man who walked past told her.

    (c) She had seen it when they drove past.

    (d) One of the four-wheel drive men who was trying to help told her.

    The best answer is ☐ .

> **Think!**
> Read paragraph 6 to find out what happened just before she raced off.

2. Explain why the ropes the men in their four-wheel drives were using snapped.

    _____

    _____

    _____

> **Think!**
> Paragraphs 4 and 5 have some information to help you answer this question.

3. Give some reasons to explain why the water was coming in the driver's window.

    _____

    _____

    _____

> **Think!**
> You will need to think about all the things that were happening to the vehicle.

4. What could the front-end loader do that the other vehicles couldn't?

    _____

> **Think!**
> Read paragraph 7 to help you answer this question.

    _____

Inferring

Think about the strategies you have learnt and work out these answers.

1. Why do you think Dad walked slowly when he got out of the boat?

    (a) He was unhappy.

    (b) His knees were sore.

    (c) He didn't want to pull the boat out.

    (d) He was thirsty.

    The best answer is ☐.

2. Which description do you think best describes the four-wheel drive owners?

    (a) helpful

    (b) good fishermen

    (c) careless

    (d) useless

    The best answer is ☐.

3. Explain some of the reasons why Ben and his mum found it so difficult to hold the boat.

    _____

    _____

    _____

    _____

4. (a) Do you think Mum had some good ideas?

    ☐ yes ☐ no

    (b) Explain why you think this.

    _____

    _____

    _____

    _____

    _____

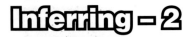

Inferring – 2

Read the report.

Favourite sports

Introduction

1. Miss Bevan was keen to encourage her pupils to be healthy and play more out-of-school sport. She wanted to find out which sports were available in the community and who played them, so the pupils could tell each other about the different sports they played.

2. After discussing the different sports, the pupils noted that Bankbridge Primary School had interschool netball and football competitions with other primary schools in the area.

3. They also found that a lot of equipment was needed for horseriding, archery was held at a venue some distance away and swimming events were conducted all year round.

4. Her class conducted a survey to find out which competitive sports the pupils in the class played, who played them and how popular they were.

Results

5. The results are shown on the table below.

Sport played	Girls	Boys	Total
Netball	12	2	14
Football	2	10	12
Basketball	2	5	7
Swimming	3	3	6
Baseball	4	0	4
Rugby	0	4	4
Tennis	2	1	3
Horseriding	2	0	2
Archery	0	1	1

Conclusion

6. The results showed that netball was the most popular sport for girls and football was the most popular with boys.

Inferring

Use the strategies you learnt and practised in **Stuck in the sand** to work out what is probably true.

- The answers are usually not in the text, but there is information to give you clues to think about. (This information could be underlined.)
- Find the answer that makes the most sense and is supported by text details.
- Always consider all the possible answers before making a decision.

---

1. *Miss Bevan wanted the pupils to tell about the sport they played because:*

   (a) she was interested in sport.

   (b) she wanted to encourage more pupils to learn about different sports so they would play them.

   (c) she thought sport was a waste of time.

   (d) she wanted everyone to play basketball.

   The best answer is ☐.

   > **Think!**
   > Read the introduction and ask yourself why she did it.

2. *Why do you think archery had the least number of pupils participating?*

   (a) It takes too long to play.

   (b) It is a hard sport to play.

   (c) It's tiring.

   (d) It takes a long time to travel to the venue.

   The best answer is ☐.

3. *Why do you think only two children participated in horseriding?*

   (a) Many children don't like horses.

   (b) You get hot while horseriding.

   (c) It is expensive.

   (d) It's hard to learn how to ride a horse.

   The best answer is ☐.

4. *The most popular out-of-school sports were netball and football. Explain a possible reason for this.*

   _____

   _____

The tests on pages 71 to 73 will show how well you can:

Conclude   Summarise   Infer

You will be working on your own.

Read the recount.

Our earthquake

1. I really can't believe it, but we had some real excitement at our school today; our very own, quite scary, earthquake.

2. It was about 11.30 and we were in class when I noticed that the room was vibrating. I didn't pay much attention because it often happens when one of those big trucks goes past our school. Then our desks started to shake and I was sure that it was Sam playing around, as usual. I was very cross with him when all my pens fell onto the floor and I started to really tell him off. He looked at me in surprise, then just pointed to the window. The blinds were moving from side to side—and it wasn't even windy.

3. Suddenly, there was dead silence. We all stopped and stared at Miss Green. She had her mouth wide open. Then she said, 'Let's get out and onto the field. Hurry!' We all rushed out. Some people looked really frightened, especially when Sam said in his usual loud voice, 'It's an earthquake isn't it, Miss?'

4. I immediately thought about tsunamis and was really worried. I imagined a huge wave rolling across the field. Then I remembered that we were on a hill and the beach was a few kilometres away. I was a bit happier, but my legs were still shaking and I felt funny.

5. We all stayed outside for quite a while. Then the head teacher came past and told us that we could have our lunch on the field, a bit earlier than usual.

6. After lunch, we went back inside and picked up things that had fallen over. We talked with Miss Green, who explained earthquakes to us. Then she asked us to write a recount about what happened to us, our families, pets and homes. We had to finish it at home.

7. I had been a bit worried about my home, but when I got there I found everything in the house was fine. Griff, my dog, was hiding under my bed, but he came out later when Mum called him. Dad had the worst time. He told us that big cracks appeared in the walls on the tenth floor of the hospital and they had to get all the patients out. He said he was really frightened.

8. I know it was all very exciting and it was on the television news for ages last night, but I really hope we don't have another one.

Name: _____ Date: _____

- Make sure you understand the question and what you are making conclusions about.
- Look in the text for facts and details and underline them.
- Decide what they mean.
- Check all possible answers before making a decision.

---

1. *You can conclude that the earthquake caused the blinds to move because ...*

   (a) they were moving.

   (b) they were moving but it wasn't windy.

   (c) the blinds were open.

   (d) the wind was blowing them.

   The best answer is ☐.

2. *What conclusion did the writer make when the room first started to vibrate?*

   (a) There was a truck going past.

   (b) Sam caused it.

   (c) It was an earthquake.

   (d) The builders caused it.

   The best answer is ☐.

3. *Explain why the writer concluded that his dad had the worst time.*

   _____

   _____

   _____

4. (a) Do you think the pupils needed to be worried about a tsunami?

   ☐ yes ☐ no

   (b) Explain why you reached this conclusion.

   _____

   _____

Name: _____ Date: _____

- Make sure you understand the question and underline any keywords.
- Decide what information is important and how it is connected.
- Omit any unnecessary or unconnected information.
- Always check all possible answers before making a decision.

---

1. *Which sentence best summarises why Miss Green told the children to get out of the classroom?*

   (a) It was lunchtime.

   (b) She was frightened.

   (c) She was concerned about their safety.

   (d) They needed some fresh air.

   I think the best answer is ☐.

2. (a) Find one word in the text that best summarises how Dad was feeling at work.

   _____

   (b) Write two words to summarise your feelings about earthquakes.

   _____   _____

3. *Write a summary of what happened at school after lunch.*

   _____

   _____

   _____

   _____

4. *Summarise the reasons why the writer thought that Sam was to blame for the strange events.*

   _____

   _____

Inferring

Name: _____ Date: _____

- The answers are usually not in the text, but there is information to give you clues to think about. (This information could be underlined.)
- Find the answer that makes the most sense and is supported by text details.
- Always consider all the possible answers before making a decision.

---

1. *Why do you think there was suddenly dead silence in the classroom?*

   (a) The teacher was talking.

   (b) Sam told everyone to be quiet.

   (c) The children all knew that something was wrong and were scared.

   (d) The head teacher came in.

   The best answer is ⬜.

2. *Why do you think the children all looked at their teacher?*

   (a) They didn't know what to do.

   (b) She told them to look at her.

   (c) She was working with them.

   (d) She stood up.

   The best answer is ⬜.

3. *Explain why you think the head teacher let the pupils have their lunch early.*

   _____

   _____

   _____

4. *Miss Green wanted the children to finish writing their reports at home.*

   Explain why they needed to do this.

   _____

   _____

   _____

The focus of this section is on the following skills:

Cause and effect	Fact or opinion	Point of view and purpose

Cause and effect

Objective

- Pupils will determine cause and effect and understand how they are connected.

Background information

Pupils need to understand that the cause leads to the effect and that they are connected.

This section demonstrates strategies for pupils to use in order to find information in text which, in turn, helps them to make the connection and determine cause and effect.

They need to find and underline the keywords in questions, then search for information in the text which makes connections between the keywords and either the cause or the effect. They need to understand that they will be given one in the question and they will need to search for the other.

Answers

Smallpox: A deadly disease .... pages 76–79

- *Practice:* page 78
  1. (c)
  2. (b)
  3. Answers should indicate the effects include developing a fever and the skin being covered by deep sores which usually left survivors with pockmarked skin.
  4. People who survived smallpox were never affected by the disease again.
- *On your own:* page 79
  1. (d)
  2. (a)
  3. The Buddhist nun ground up smallpox scabs from infected people and blew the powder into people's noses, a process called variolation.
  4. The mild reaction was caused by Dr Jenner taking fluid from a milkmaid's cowpox and scratching it into the arms of the gardener's son.

Healthy weight loss .... pages 80–81

- *Try it out:* page 81
  1. (c)
  2. Teacher check
  3. The writer does not want people to go on crash diets, miss out on eating from the important food groups or waste money on expensive weight loss treatments or programmes.
  4. (a) The writer wants people to take a common sense, healthy and inexpensive approach to losing weight.
     (b)–(c) Teacher check

Fact or opinion

Objective

- Pupils will demonstrate their ability to identify facts and opinions and their understanding of how they differ.

Background information

A fact is something that is true. It can be verified by referring to other information. In other words, it can be checked and be shown to be correct.

An opinion is something that someone believes to be true, but which cannot be verified. In other words, it is something that someone thinks rather than knows is true.

Pupils must be able to distinguish between facts and opinions in order to become critical readers. They have to engage and interact with text and read with a questioning attitude. They can then look for relationships and critically judge and evaluate what they read, identifying facts and opinions.

Critical readers become more discriminating consumers of the news media and advertising; an important life skill.

Answers

The Channel Tunnel .... pages 82–85

- *Practice:* page 84
  1. (c)
  2. Fact: The central tunnel met in the middle on 1 December 1990.
     Opinion: They were all very pleased.
  3. (a) Opinion
     (b) It is an opinion because the writer believes it to be true and it can't be checked.
  4. (d)
- *On your own:* page 85
  1. (c)
  2. (b)
  3. (a) Opinion
     (b) Teacher check
  4. Fact: Trains carried about 28 million passengers on the Tunnel rail passenger service. Opinion: The writer said it happened 'a short time later', which is an opinion.

The blue-ringed octopus .... pages 86–87

- *Try it out:* page 87
  1. (b)
  2. (a) Fact: The sailor picked up a blue-ringed octopus.
     (b) Opinion: poor and young
  3. (a)
  4. Teacher check
  5. Teacher check

The focus of this section is on the following skills:

Cause and effect	Fact or opinion	Point of view and purpose

Point of view and purpose

Objective
- Pupils will understand and identify the writer's point of view and purpose.

Background information
The writer's point of view is his or her opinion about a subject. A reader should, after careful and detailed analysis of what has been written, understand and be able to identify the point of view expressed in the text. This information can be explicit but it is often implicit in the text.

The writer's purpose for writing explains *why* the text was written. It may be to express a particular point of view, to amuse, to entertain, to inform, to persuade, to instruct, to describe, to record information or to explain something.

Pupils should be encouraged to work out how and what the writer was thinking and to use this to help them make decisions about the writer's point of view. They should then look for details in the text to support or reject the choices they have made. (These can be underlined.) All possible choices should be considered before a final decision is made.

Answers

Christmas cards .... pages 88–91
- *Practice:* page 90
  1. Possible answers: finding the first card in the letterbox, guessing who sent it, displaying them in different ways, hearing from people once a year, getting a photo
  2. (c)
  3. Teacher check
  4. Teacher check
- *On your own:* page 91
  1. (a)
  2. (c)
  3. Teacher check
  4. Teacher check
  5. Teacher check

Pocket money .... pages 92–93
- *Try it out:* page 93
  1. (c)
  2. (b)
  3. (a)
  4. Answers should indicate that his pocket money gets less each time he does something wrong until he ends up with none.
  5. Teacher check

Pupil tests

Tests have been incorporated to provide teachers with a clear record of each pupil's level of understanding and development pertaining to each skill. It is important that pupils work independently to complete the tests.

A class test record sheet and pupil evaluation sheet are provided on pages viii and ix.

Letter *(pages 94–97)*

Answers
- ***Test 1****: Cause and effect* .... (Page 95)
  1. (b)
  2. (d)
  3. They had difficulty because the tent gear was soaked by the rain and hard to handle.
  4. Possible answers: They missed out on lunch, they were starving, they got mad, they fell into the water, they got cold and wet.
  5. (b)
  6. She found them hidden in their pockets and they were not allowed to eat on the bus.

- ***Test 2****: Fact or opinion* .... (Page 96)
  1. (b)
  2. (a)
  3. (d)
  4. (a) Fact
     (b) Teacher check
  5. Fact: We stopped for a snack.
     Opinion: We were weak with hunger.

- ***Test 3****: Point of view and purpose* .... (Page 97)
  1. (c) (Others may be accepted if justified)
  2. (d)
  3. (b)
  4. Teacher check
  5. Teacher check

Cause and effect – 1

Cause and effect is when one thing (the cause) makes something happen (the effect).

If you want to understand what you read you must be to be able to work out the cause and effect of the things that happen.

Read the report.

Smallpox: A deadly disease

1. For centuries, smallpox was responsible for the death of millions of people. Those infected became very ill, developed a fever and their skin was covered with deep sores. The people who survived had pockmarked skin for the rest of their lives.

2. Smallpox is believed to have started in Africa and to have spread to India and China. The first recorded smallpox epidemic was in 1350 BCE during an Egyptian war. Between the fifth and seventh centuries, smallpox reached Europe and by the eighteenth century epidemics were common in the major European cities. There were also epidemics in the colonies of North America. Smallpox was a deadly, frightening disease that spread to all areas of the world, except for Australia and a few isolated islands.

3. People realised that anyone who managed to survive smallpox was never affected by the disease again. In the eleventh century, a Buddhist nun tried to give people a milder form of smallpox by grinding up scabs from infected people and blowing the powder into their noses. This was called *variolation*. It became very popular in China, India and Turkey and by the seventeenth century it was used in Europe. Most people survived a milder form of the disease, but others died. The overall number of deaths was, however, greatly reduced.

4. An English doctor, called Jenner, noticed that milkmaids who developed a similar but less serious disease called cowpox, did not get smallpox. In 1796, he took some of the fluid from a milkmaid's cowpox and scratched the arms of the gardener's son and applied it. The boy became mildly ill, but six weeks later when he exposed the boy to smallpox, he didn't become infected. Doctor Jenner was the first to use the word vaccine which he made up from *vacca*, the Latin word for a cow. People didn't believe his vaccine would work, but by 1800 more than 100 000 people had been vaccinated. His research was responsible for saving millions of lives.

5. In 1967, the World Health Organisation started a worldwide vaccination programme to eradicate smallpox. They achieved success and by 1980 they were able to declare that the world was at last smallpox-free.

Cause and effect

Learn how you can work out the cause and effect.

- The cause leads to the effect and they are connected.
- You will be told one and you will need to work out the other.
- Look for keywords in the question and underline them.
- Find words in the text that are connected to the key question words.
- Always check all possible answers before making a decision.

---

1. *Why didn't all the people in Australia need to be vaccinated against smallpox?*

   (a) There are lots of cows in Australia.

   (b) They drink lots of milk.

   (c) They all had cowpox.

   (d) There wasn't any smallpox in Australia.

   Choosing the best answer.

   (a) There are lots of cows, but that is not the cause for Australians not needing vaccinations. Not a good answer.

   (b) There is nothing in the text about drinking milk, so this can't be the right answer.

   (c) There is nothing in the text about Australians having cowpox. Not a good answer.

   (d) The text says that there hasn't been any smallpox disease in Australia, so this is the reason why people didn't need to be vaccinated. This is the best answer.

2. *What effect did cowpox have on people?*

   (a) They died of smallpox.

   (b) They didn't get smallpox.

   (c) They got a milder form of smallpox.

   (d) They got very ill.

   Choosing the best answer.

   (a) The milkmaids who got cowpox didn't get smallpox, so they couldn't have died from it. Not the right answer.

   (b) The text says that because they had cowpox, the milkmaids did not get smallpox. This is a very good answer, but remember to check all answers.

   (c) Variolation, not cowpox, caused many people to have a milder form of smallpox. This is not the best answer.

   (d) Cowpox did not make people very ill. This is not the best answer.

Cause and effect

Use similar strategies to those on page 77 to practise working out cause and effect. (Clues are given to help you.)

1. **What effect did the World Health Organisation vaccination programme have on smallpox?**

    (a) It made people more aware of the problem.

    (b) It reduced smallpox epidemics.

    (c) It eradicated smallpox.

    (d) It raised money to help countries with smallpox.

    The best answer is ☐.

    > **Think!**
    > All the sentences are true. Find the words 'World Health Organisation' and read that paragraph very carefully to decide on the best answer.

2. **What caused doctors to stop vaccinating people against smallpox?**

    (a) They found it was too expensive.

    (b) They didn't need to.

    (c) It didn't work.

    (d) They didn't have enough people to do it.

    The best answer is ☐.

    > **Think!**
    > Read the last two paragraphs.

3. **What effects does smallpox have on the body?**

    _____

    _____

    _____

    > **Think!**
    > Find the definition of smallpox and describe the effects.

4. **What happened to people who managed to survive smallpox?**

    _____

    _____

    _____

    > **Think!**
    > Read paragraph 3.

Cause and effect

On your own

Think about the strategies you have been using and work out these answers.

1. What happened when people finally saw the effect of Jenner's vaccine?

    (a) They didn't believe it worked.

    (b) They thought he was stupid.

    (c) They didn't want to be vaccinated.

    (d) Thousands of people were vaccinated.

    The best answer is ☐.

2. What caused very badly pockmarked skin?

    (a) the smallpox sores

    (b) variolation

    (c) fever

    (d) vaccination

    The best answer is ☐.

3. Explain what the Buddhist nun did to cause the reduction of deaths from smallpox.

    _____

    _____

    _____

    _____

    _____

4. Explain what caused the gardener's son to have a mild reaction when he was exposed to cowpox.

    _____

    _____

    _____

    _____

    _____

Read the discussion text.

Healthy weight loss

1. I believe that it is time for some plain common sense about losing weight.

2. Being overweight is serious and an increasing problem, especially for children. It is destroying their health and, in some cases, causing great unhappiness. I am not arguing that there isn't a problem, just what should be done about it.

3. Weight loss can be so simple but you shouldn't expect it to happen quickly. Research has shown how unhealthy it is for your weight to go up and down as it often does when people follow crash diets.

4. It makes me angry to see the amount of time and money people waste on expensive weight loss treatments and programmes. What is even more worrying is that so many people are putting their health at risk with some of these fad crash diets, especially those that do not allow food from some of the important food groups.

5. There are only two simple rules to follow to lose weight or to maintain a healthy weight. They are to eat a balanced diet with less fat and sugar and to exercise more.

6. You don't have to starve to lose weight. If you eat fewer sweet things like chocolates, cakes and biscuits; eat more fruit and vegetables; drink water instead of soft drinks and juices; and reduce fats by eating less fried food, you will lose weight and be healthier.

7. You don't need to pay a lot of money to join a gym or buy expensive equipment. Exercise should be part of your everyday life, like walking or cycling instead of going by car. You need to be more active, instead of watching TV or sitting at a computer. Start some organised activity you'll keep up because you enjoy it.

8. It is important that you continue with your lifestyle changes, not just for a few days, weeks or months. Of course, sometimes you will eat the wrong foods and that is fine as long as it only happens occasionally and you normally eat, drink and exercise wisely.

9. It really shouldn't be too complicated, difficult or expensive to lose weight or maintain a healthy weight. You just need to be patient and make some changes to your life. If you do, you can be healthier and have a much better future without spending a lot of money and making a lot of other people very rich.

Cause and effect

Use the strategies you learnt and practised in **Smallpox: A deadly disease** to work out cause and effect.

- The cause leads to the effect and they are connected.
- You will be told one and you will need to work out the other.
- Look for keywords in the question and underline them.
- Find words in the text that are connected to the key question words.
- Always check all possible answers before making a decision.

---

1. *What is one effect of crash diets?*

    (a) You are healthier.

    (b) Your weight loss is usually maintained.

    (c) Your weight loss is often fast.

    (d) Your diet is well balanced.

    The best answer is ☐.

2. *Describe some of the healthy, inexpensive things you can do to lose weight.*

    _____

    _____

3. *What are some of the things the writer does not want people to do to cause them to lose weight?*

    _____

    _____

4. (a) What effect does the writer want to achieve by writing this text?

    _____

    _____

    (b) Do you agree with the writer?   ☐ yes   ☐ no

    (c) Describe the effect this text had on you.

    _____

    _____

When reading, it is important to understand the difference between facts and opinions and to be able to work out which is which.

A **fact** is something that is true. An **opinion** is something that someone believes is true.
Read the report.

The Channel Tunnel

1. One of the greatest engineering projects of the twentieth century was the construction of the tunnel under the English Channel. It is the world's second longest underground tunnel and the longest underwater tunnel. The Channel Tunnel provides the first land link between Europe and Britain since they were separated during the Ice Age, about 40 million years ago.

2. There are, in fact, three separate tunnels— each 50 km long—between England and France. Fast trains travel in different directions along two tunnels, each 7.6 m in diameter. The third, a narrower central tunnel, is used for ventilation and for maintenance, and can also be used as an escape route in an emergency.

3. After much discussion and negotiation, the British and French governments signed the Channel Tunnel Treaty. When work began in 1987, everyone was very happy to see it finally underway. They had been considering such a project since the time of Napoleon. Interestingly, in 1802, a French engineer proposed a tunnel to be used by horse-drawn carriages and lit with gas lamps. His ambitious plan included an island in the middle where the horses could come up and be rested and the passengers could get some fresh air.

4. The Tunnel was very expensive, costing twice as much as estimated. The French started tunnelling from France and the English from England and they were all very pleased when their central tunnel met in the middle on 1 December 1990, some 40 m below the seabed. About 1500 workers had spent over seven years on the project. The English and the French had worked hard, both teams attempting to reach the middle first. The English won. Work on the main tunnels was continued until they met in May and June the next year.

5. Queen Elizabeth II and President Mitterrand opened the Tunnel in May 1994. A short time later, the Tunnel rail passenger service began. Trains carried about 28 million passengers in the first five years and also transported vehicles and freight between the two countries. It only takes about 20 minutes and it is a popular option for both residents and tourists, who can take their vehicles on the train.

6. Unfortunately, the project hasn't made a lot of money and has been running at a loss. The owners haven't yet paid back the money they borrowed.

Fact or opinion

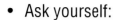

Learning about the skill

Learn how you can work out if something is a fact or an opinion.

- Ask yourself:

  Can the statement be checked and proved to be correct? If it can, it is a fact.

  Is it what someone thinks is true and can't be proved? If so, it is an opinion.

  For example: Hens lay eggs. (fact)

  Eggs taste good. (opinion)

- Always check all the possible answers before making a decision.

---

1. Which sentence states an opinion?

(a) Queen Elizabeth and President Mitterrand officially opened the tunnel.

(b) About 1500 workers built the tunnel.

(c) The tunnel is 40 m below the seabed.

(d) Tourists like the tunnel.

Choosing the best answer.

(a) This is a fact that would be easy to check; for example, in newspaper articles, photos, film and in books. Not a good answer.

(b) The number of workers employed on the project would be recorded and so this is a fact that could be checked. This is not the right answer.

(c) This information could be checked and is a fact, so it is not a good answer.

(d) It is true that some tourists use the tunnel but there isn't any way to check that tourists really like the tunnel. This is an opinion. It is the best answer.

2. Which sentence has both a fact and an opinion?

(a) The central tunnel is smaller and is used for maintenance.

(b) The Channel Tunnel, built in the 20th century, was a great engineering feat.

(c) Passengers, vehicles and freight are transported through the tunnel.

(d) The tunnel is great and I wish I could go through it.

Choosing the best answer.

(a) This sentence has two facts that can be checked. The central tunnel is smaller and it is used for maintenance. This isn't the right answer.

(b) It is a fact that the tunnel was built in the 20th century, but while some people may think it was a great engineering feat others may not, so this is an opinion. This answer has a fact and an opinion.

(c) These three bits of information are facts and can be proved to be correct. Not the right answer.

(d) There are two opinions in this sentence, so it is not the correct answer.

Fact or opinion

Use similar strategies to those on page 83 to practise working out fact and opinion. (Clues are given to help you.)

1. Which sentence is an opinion?

    (a) The tunnels are 50 km long.

    (b) The central tunnel can be used in an emergency.

    (c) The trains are fast.

    (d) Trains travel along two of the tunnels.

    The best answer is ☐.

    > **Think!**
    > Which one is a matter of opinion and depends on what you are comparing it with?

2. Read the sentence from the text and write one fact and one opinion.

    > They were all very pleased when their central tunnel met in the middle on 1 December 1990.

    Fact: _____

    _____

    Opinion: _____

    _____

    > **Think!**
    > There is one fact and one opinion. Write each one as a sentence.

3. Read this sentence from the text.

    > Everyone was very happy to see it underway.

    (a) Is it fact or opinion? _____

    (b) Explain why you think this.

    _____

    _____

    _____

    > **Think!**
    > A fact is something that can be shown to be true.
    >
    > Find the sentence in the text and think about it.

4. Which sentence is a fact?

    (a) The third tunnel is narrow.

    (b) The tunnel is extremely long.

    (c) It takes a short time to go through the tunnel.

    (d) The tunnel took over seven years to build.

    The best answer is ☐.

    > **Think!**
    > Which sentence does not state an opinion?

Fact or opinion

Think about the strategies you have been using and work out these answers.

1. *Which sentence is a fact?*

    (a) The trains are very fast.

    (b) The tunnel was very expensive.

    (c) The trains carried about 28 million passengers in the first five years.

    (d) Travelling by train through the tunnel is popular.

    The best answer is ☐.

2. *Which sentence is not a fact?*

    (a) About 1500 workers were employed to construct the tunnel.

    (b) A French engineer had an ambitious plan.

    (c) The tunnels met about 40 m below the seabed.

    (d) Work on the tunnel began in 1987.

    The best answer is ☐.

3. (a) Is this sentence from the text a fact or an opinion? _____

    Unfortunately, the project hasn't made a lot of money.

    (b) Explain your answer.

    _____

    _____

    _____

4. *Read the sentence from the text and write one fact and one opinion.*

    A short time later, the tunnel rail passenger service began and trains carried about 28 million passengers.

    Fact: _____

    _____

    Opinion: _____

    _____

Read the report.

The blue-ringed octopus

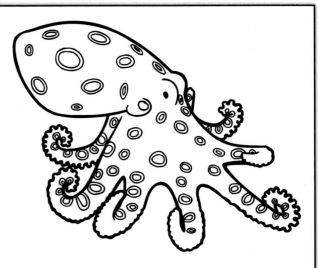

1. The blue-ringed octopus is the most feared of all small sea creatures. It has enough toxin in its small body to kill about 26 people in minutes and there is no known antidote. However, it should be remembered that this golfball-sized creature is not aggressive. It normally only bites when it feels threatened, as it does if it is picked up or stepped on.

2. A blue-ringed octopus is usually a pale brown to yellow colour when resting. Its fluorescent blue spots only appear when it is provoked. It has eight arms, on which suckers are attached, and a sack-like body. Like all octopuses (or octopi), it can grow another arm to replace one that is lost. Its beak is sharp and can penetrate a wetsuit.

3. It was only after a spearfisherman was bitten in Darwin in 1954 that it was realised this octopus could be dangerous. The poor young sailor had picked up a dangerous blue-ringed octopus and placed it on his shoulder for a few minutes as he was heading back to shore with his friend. They were very puzzled when his mouth became dry and he had trouble breathing. He started to vomit and was immediately taken to hospital when he stopped breathing. After his death, they discovered a small bite mark on his shoulder.

4. A bite is not immediately painful, but after ten to fifteen minutes the toxin circulates through the body and the symptoms develop very quickly. Paralysis occurs and the patient stops breathing and requires mouth-to-mouth resuscitation. If victims survive for over twelve hours, they usually recover without any lasting effects from this terrible experience.

5. Blue-ringed octopuses are found in shallow water and small rock pools around the coast of Australia, although they have been found at depths of 50 metres. They feed on small crabs, shrimp and fish, which they bite with their beak and then suck out the flesh.

6. The life span of a blue-ringed octopus is short. A female lays up to 100 eggs which she carries under her arms. The male dies after mating. The eggs hatch in 50 days and, because the female has not been eating during this time, she dies. The young octopuses are the size of a pea but they grow and mature quickly.

7. The blue-ringed octopus is a fascinating creature but it can be extremely dangerous. It should be treated with respect and never be picked up.

Fact or opinion

Use the strategies you learnt and practised in *The Channel Tunnel* to work out facts and opinions.

- Ask yourself:
  Can the statement be checked and proved to be correct? If it can, it is a fact.
  Is it what someone thinks is true and can't be proved? If so, it is an opinion.
- Always check all the possible answers before making a decision.

---

1. *Which sentence states an opinion?*
   (a) There is no known antidote for a blue-ringed octopus bite.
   (b) Being bitten by a blue-ringed octopus is a terrible experience.
   (c) A female blue-ringed octopus lays up to 100 eggs.
   (d) A blue-ringed octopus has eight arms.

   The best answer is ☐.

   > **Think!**
   > Facts can be checked, opinions can't. Which sentence tells what someone thinks?

2. *Read the sentence from the text.*
   (a) Write a short sentence with a fact.

      The poor, young sailor picked up a blue-ringed octopus.

      Fact: _____

      _____

   (b) Which two words express an opinion?

      _____   _____

3. *Which sentence is not a fact?*
   (a) Blue-ringed octopuses are fascinating creatures.
   (b) Blue-ringed octopuses are found in rock pools.
   (c) The male dies after mating.
   (d) Symptoms develop about 10 to 15 minutes after being bitten.

   The best answer is ☐.

4. *Write one fact from the report.*

   _____

5. *What is your opinion of blue-ringed octopuses?*

   _____

   _____

   _____

Point of view and purpose – 1

When we read, we should try to think like the writer to work out how and what he or she feels and believes (point of view) about the subject and why he or she wrote the text (purpose).

Read the discussion text.

Christmas cards

1. I love receiving Christmas cards. I love buying or making them and then writing in them, putting on the stamps and popping them in the letterbox one at a time. I am so excited when I find the very first Christmas card in our letterbox. I try to guess who could have sent it before I open it, read it and put it up where everyone can see it. Christmas cards are wonderful.

2. There are some people who complain they are too expensive. They say they cost too much to buy and that the money spent on stamps is wasted when an email is free. But some people, like my grandparents, don't have a computer. Anyway, a computer message is so dull, colourless and boring. I think Christmas cards are worth the cost. I don't buy expensive ones and I usually make most of my cards. Even the post office understands how important Christmas cards are because it puts out special Christmas stamps and they are just gorgeous.

3. Other people are concerned about the time it takes to write individual cards when you can very quickly email the same message to all your friends and family. I think cards should be made or bought specially for each person and that the messages in them should be just meant for that person too. The time that cards take to be delivered also worries some people, but I can't see that it is a problem; you just have to get started earlier. Anyway, I think you should make time for people you care about.

4. Christmas cards are beautiful. They are so colourful and come in so many different shapes and sizes. I love the traditional ones, especially those with snow scenes and those that come from other countries. Some of them are so different and interesting. They make me realise that Christmas is celebrated in many faraway places and in so many different ways. I have so much fun working out different ways of displaying them.

5. Christmas is a time for giving and sharing with all people, especially the ones who are important to us. There are lots of people I only hear from at Christmas time when they send me a card and tell me what's been happening in their lives. Often they include a photo and I enjoy seeing their smiling faces again. Some of my friends make Christmas cards using a family photo. I think this is a really great idea.

6. I can't imagine Christmas without cards because for me they are one of the great joys of this special time. There is no way in the world that the cost or the time involved will stop me from sharing them with the people I care about.

Point of view and purpose

Learn how to try to work out the writer's point of view and his or her probable purpose or reason for writing the text.

- Writers don't always just tell you what they think or believe or why they have written the text. Sometimes you have to try to think like they do and work it out for yourself.
- In the text, there are details and information related to the question for you to find, underline and use in making your choices.
- Always consider all possible answers before making a decision.

---

1. *The writer believes that:*
   - (a) Emails are better than Christmas cards because they save time.
   - (b) Emails are more personal than Christmas cards.
   - (c) Everyone should send emails at Christmas time.
   - (d) Christmas cards are worth the extra time.

   Choosing the best answer.
   - (a) It is true that in paragraph 3 the writer does say that emails are quicker than cards, but not that they are better, so this is not a good answer.
   - (b) The writer says that cards are more personal because you need to make or buy them and write an individual message inside. This is not a good answer.
   - (c) The writer says that emails are not as good as cards. He or she wouldn't want people to send them. This is not the correct answer.
   - (d) The writer says Christmas cards take longer and that people should make time to do them. This is the best answer.

2. *The writer probably wrote the text because he or she:*
   - (a) hates computers.
   - (b) is worried that people are going to stop sending Christmas cards.
   - (c) likes Christmas cards.
   - (d) likes the 'good old days'.

   Choosing the best answer.
   - (a) The writer doesn't say anything about computers, just that cards are better than emails. This is not the right answer.
   - (b) The writer likes Christmas cards and wants people to send them and could be worried that people will stop sending them. This is a possible reason for writing the text. This is a very good answer but you must consider all of them.
   - (c) It is true, the writer does like Christmas cards, but this doesn't fully explain his or her reason for writing the text. Not the best answer.
   - (d) There is nothing in the text about 'the good old days'. This is not the best answer.

Practice page

Use similar strategies to those on page 89 to help you work out what the writer believes about the subject and why he or she wrote the text. (Clues are given to help you.)

1. List some of the things the writer enjoys about receiving Christmas cards.

_____

_____

_____

_____

> **Think!**
> Read all of the text and underline any information about receiving cards before starting your list.

2. Which of these is not what the writer believes?

   (a) Christmas cards are worth the time and the money they cost.

   (b) Christmas cards are very attractive.

   (c) Christmas stamps cost too much.

   (d) Christmas cards from other countries are interesting.

   The best answer is ☐.

> **Think!**
> There are keywords in each sentence that will help you to find the details you need in the text.

3. Explain how the writer thinks Christmas cards help people to keep in touch.

_____

_____

_____

> **Think!**
> Read paragraph 5 carefully.

4. Explain your own point of view about Christmas cards.

_____

_____

_____

> **Think!**
> How do you agree and disagree with the writer?

Point of view and purpose

Think about the strategies you have learnt and work out these answers.

1. What does the writer think people should do to make sure their cards arrive on time?

    (a) Start earlier.

    (b) Buy, not make all their cards.

    (c) Not send so many cards.

    (d) Send emails instead.

    The best answer is ☐.

2. Which sentence do you think the writer would probably disagree with?

    (a) Christmas is a time for friends and family.

    (b) It's great to hear news about people who are important to us.

    (c) The best thing about Christmas is the holidays.

    (d) Christmas is a happy time.

    The best answer is ☐.

3. (a) Think of four words you could use to describe the writer.

    I think the writer is:

    _____

    _____

    _____

    _____

    (b) Explain why you think this (your point of view).

    _____

    _____

    _____

    _____

    _____

4. The writer described emails as 'dull, colourless and boring'.

    (a) Do you agree?

    ☐ yes ☐ no

    (b) Explain your point of view.

    _____

    _____

    _____

5. The writer's purpose in writing the text was to persuade people to keep sending cards. How well do you think he or she achieved this purpose?

    (a) very well

    (b) quite well

    (c) not well

    (d) not at all

    I think the best answer is ☐.

Read the poem.

Pocket money

Fridays—
They should be
Our pocket money days.

Payment
For slaving
From Monday to Sunday

My sis
Gets paid always
She buys things—she saves!

But for me
There's another story
I'm the poorest of slaves!

If I don't
Hang my clothes up
My money is less.

If I'm late
Home for dinner,
It goes down—how did you guess?

If my manners
Are not perfect,
Or I'm not acting fair

My money
Goes down 'til
My pockets are bare!

Daily I wish—
And some days I pray—
That one Friday will be
My pocket money day!

Point of view and purpose

Use the strategies you learnt and practised in **Christmas cards** to work out the writer's point of view and purpose.

- Writers don't always just tell you what they think or believe or why they have written the text. Sometimes you have to try to think like they do and work it out for yourself.

- In the text, there are details and information related to the question for you to find and use in making your choices. (These could be underlined.)

- Always consider all possible answers before making a decision.

---

1. *What do you think the writer thinks about his sister?*

   (a) She doesn't deserve to get pocket money.

   (b) She doesn't have to do jobs.

   (c) She gets pocket money and he doesn't.

   (d) She should work harder.

   The best answer is ☐.

   > **Think!**
   > Read the part about his sister then think carefully about each answer.

2. *Why do you think the writer wrote this poem?*

   (a) He wanted to make people laugh.

   (b) He wants people to feel sorry for him.

   (c) He is happy.

   (d) He wants people to hate his sister.

   The best answer is ☐.

3. *What would the writer have to do to get pocket money on Fridays?*

   (a) Be more organised and polite.

   (b) Help his sister.

   (c) Think of more jobs he could do.

   (d) Be happy.

   The best answer is ☐.

4. *Explain why the writer's parents don't give him pocket money.*

   _____

   _____

   _____

   _____

5. *Explain your point of view about pocket money.*

   _____

   _____

   _____

   _____

The tests on pages 95 to 97 will show how well you can work out:

Cause and effect   Fact or opinion   Point of view and purpose

You will be working on your own.

Read the report.

Letter

Dear Mum and Dad,

1. This school camp I've been looking forward to for months is a disaster.

2. I am cold, wet, hungry and miserable and you have to come down and get me right away. If you don't it will be too late. By the time camp ends next Friday I will probably have caught the flu and be dead or at least be really sick and stuck in the local hospital. So please come and rescue me now.

3. This place is such a long way from home and we seemed to travel all day to get here. The bus trip started okay but we weren't allowed to eat in the bus. By the time we finally stopped for a snack, we were weak with hunger. Mr Jeans had organised sandwiches, fruit and bottled water. Boy, did the chips in the service station shop smell good! While we were there, Miss Weston found the crisps and chocolate bars we'd hidden in our pockets and threw them in the bin. How unfair was that?

4. When we arrived, they said we had to put up our tents before lunch. Taj, Simon and I wandered off and found some big nuts and threw them into the lake. They said lunch was ready. We were starving, but they wouldn't let us eat because our stupid tent wasn't up. We were really mad so we decided to go and look around the lake. There are some flat rocks near the edge and we ran and jumped on them, but they were slippery and we ended up in the water. Boy, was it cold!

5. On the way back it started to rain. All our gear was wet. They hadn't even put it away in their tents for us. Then Mr Jeans made us put up our tent by ourselves, out in the rain. The tent was all wet and hard to handle. How mean was that? Everyone stayed in the dry, warm, comfortable hall playing fun games while we were outside, dripping wet, trying to sort out the stupid tent. How unfair was that?

6. When we had finished and put our soggy, muddy gear away inside our tent, Mr Jeans said we could have a shower. Just because we left the showers running and flooded the place while we took turns to skate across the slippery floor, he said we had to stay in our tent until morning. Then he said that if we were very good, he might remember to bring us something to eat later. I think this is called torture and it's against the law, isn't it?

7. So, Mum and Dad, I'm sitting in this cold, wet tent feeling hungry and miserable, writing in the dark with only a small torch. It is all so unfair. I can't understand why they keep picking on me. Please, please come and rescue me before these unfair monsters kill me.

Love from Shane

Cause and effect

Name: _____ Date: _____

- The cause leads to the effect and they are connected.
- You will be told one and you will need to work out the other.
- Look for keywords in the question and underline them.
- Find words in the text that are connected to the key question words.
- Check all possible answers before making a decision.

---

1. *What does Shane think will happen if his parents don't come and get him?*

   (a) He will be happy.

   (b) He will be very sick or even dead.

   (c) His teachers will be angry with him.

   (d) His friends will all hate him.

   The best answer is ☐.

2. *Why did Shane and his friends fall into the lake?*

   (a) They didn't look where they were going.

   (b) They wanted to have a swim.

   (c) They were hot.

   (d) The rocks were slippery.

   The best answer is ☐.

3. *Explain why the three boys had difficulty putting up their tent.*

   _____

   _____

   _____

   _____

4. *List some of the effects caused by the boys not putting up their tent when they first arrived.*

   _____

   _____

   _____

   _____

5. *What caused Shane's teachers to punish him?*

   (a) They didn't like him.

   (b) He didn't do as he was told.

   (c) He wanted to go home.

   (d) He was a bully.

   The best answer is ☐.

6. *What caused Miss Weston to throw crisps and chocolate bars into the bin?*

   _____

   _____

   _____

Name: _____ Date: _____

- A fact can be checked and proved to be correct.
- An opinion is what someone believes to be true, but it can't be checked.
- Always check all possible answers before making a decision.

---

1. **Which sentence states an opinion?**

   (a) It started to rain.

   (b) We were starving.

   (c) There are some flat rocks near the edge of the lake.

   (d) We put our gear in the tent.

   The best answer is ☐.

2. **Which sentence is a fact?**

   (a) They threw nuts into the lake.

   (b) This place is a long way from home.

   (c) The tent was hard to handle.

   (d) The camp is a disaster.

   The best answer is ☐.

3. **Which sentence is not an opinion?**

   (a) If you don't come, it will be too late.

   (b) The bus trip started okay.

   (c) The chips smelt good.

   (d) Mr Jeans said we could have a shower.

   The best answer is ☐.

4. (a) Is this sentence from the text a fact or an opinion?

   We ended up in the water.

   _____

   (b) Explain why you think this.

   _____

   _____

   _____

   _____

5. **Write one fact and one opinion in this sentence from the text.**

   When we stopped for a snack we were weak with hunger.

   Fact:

   _____

   _____

   _____

   Opinion:

   _____

   _____

Name: _____ Date: _____

- Writers don't always tell you what they believe, you may have to work it out.
- There are details and information you can find, underline and use to help you to do this.
- Always consider all possible answers before making a decision.

---

1. **Why do you think Shane wrote this letter?**

   (a) He was unhappy.

   (b) He didn't want to stay at camp.

   (c) He wanted his parents to come and get him.

   (d) He thought everyone was picking on him.

   The best answer is ☐.

2. **Which sentence do you think Shane would probably disagree with?**

   (a) Teachers are mean.

   (b) Camping is no fun.

   (c) School camps should be banned.

   (d) It is important to be responsible and to look after your own things.

   The best answer is ☐.

3. **Shane's teachers probably think that he ...**

   (a) is a responsible pupil.

   (b) needs to be more responsible.

   (c) is a bad person.

   (d) should go home.

   The best answer is ☐.

4. (a) Think of four words to describe Shane.

   I think Shane is:

   _____

   _____

   _____

   _____

   (b) Explain why you think this (your point of view).

   _____

   _____

   _____

   _____

5. (a) Do you think Shane believes other people should look after him?

   ☐ yes ☐ no

   (b) Explain why you think this.

   _____

   _____

   _____

   _____